(1.95)

DEL OF

AIR BASES
Hoffman,
Rowen,

ISRAEL'S OCCUPATION O
WEST BANK: THE FIRST TWO
Ann Mosely Lesch,
August 1970, RM-6296-ARPA

AIRCRAFT PLANNED INS
I. K. Cohen, June 1972, R-

THE VIOLATION OF ARMS-CONTROL AGREEMENT
DETERRENCE VS. DETECTION
Fred C. Iklé, August 1960, RM-2609-ARPA

METRIC: A MULTI-E
C. C. Sherbrooke, No

NETICS AND
ZZLE DESIGN
August 1950, R-203

POLICE CIVIL SERVICE SELECTION PROCEDURES IN
NEW YORK CITY: COMPARISON OF ETHNIC GROUPS
Jan M. Chaiken and Bernard Cohen, May 1973, R-1289-NYC

IMPORTANCE OF OBSERVATION TH
STARS DON'T TWINKLE OUTSIDE
THE EARTH'S ATMOSPHERE
Walter Cunningham,
Leona Marshall Libby,
March 1969, P-4062

HABITABLE PLANETS
FOR MAN
Stephen H. Dole,
Blaisdell, 1964

E 1970s
or,
7-DOS

LINEAR PROGRAMMING AND
ECONOMIC THEORY
Paul A. Samuelson,
May 1955, P-685

THE SIMULATION
HUMAN THOUG
A. Newell and H. A.
December 1959, R

EQUENCES
October 1955,

THE SOVIET UNION IN A PERIOD
OF STRATEGIC PARITY
Herbert Goldhamer,
November 1971, R-889-PR

THE ECONOMICS OF DEFENS
IN THE NUCLEAR AGE
Charles J. Hitch and R. N. McKear
March 1960, R-346, or
Harvard University Press, 1960

MEASURING
AIRCRAFT
Arthur J. Alexan
May 1972, R-1

CABLE TELEVISION: CITIZEN
PARTICIPATION IN PLANNING
Robert K. Yin,
March 1973, R-1136-NSF

ARMS INTERACTIONS
AND ARMS CONTROL
James R. Schlesinger,
September 1968, P-3881

IS AND
N SCHOOLS
Karweit,
tions,1972

SYSTEMS ANALYSIS AND
URBAN PLANNING
Charles J. Zwick,
June 1963, P-2754

THE ROLE OF PROTOTYPES
B. H. Klein, T. K. Glennan, Jr.,
and G. H. Shubert, February 1

OF A FOCUSED LASER
ULENT ATMOSPHERE
une 1971, R-608-ARPA

UNITED STATES POLICY IN THE MIDDLE E.
CONSTRAINTS AND CHOICES
William B. Q
M-5980

ET ATT
ret Mea
raw-Hil

RACE DIFFERENCES IN INC
bert Wohlstetter, Sinclair
er 1970, R-578-OEO

MEDICAL COSTS, HEALTH INSURANCE,
AND PUBLIC POLICY
Joseph P. Newhouse and Vincent Taylor,
March 1970, P-4274-1

PRELIMINARY DESIGN OF
AN EXPERIMENTAL
-CIRCLING SPACESHIP
1946, SM-11827

GNETIC RADIATION
CLEAR EXPLOSION IN
W. J. Karzas and R. L.
October 1961, RM-2

RNATIVES IN
HOOL FINANCE
1971,

D1213003

Rand

25TH ANNIVERSARY VOLUME

25th
Year

Rand
SANTA MONICA, CA. 90406

*... a nonprofit corporation formed to further and promote
scientific, educational, and charitable purposes, all for the
public welfare and security of the United States of America.*
—Articles of Incorporation

THE RAND CORPORATION

1700 Main Street
Santa Monica, California 90406

2100 M Street, N.W.
Washington, D.C. 20037

Foreword

This year is Rand's 25th anniversary. A milestone year for any institution, the occasion creates opportunities: for stocktaking and reflecting about purposes; for looking back to beginnings; for thinking about the path ahead. In various ways Rand is doing all of these things. This book is one of those ways.

One purpose of these pages is to say something about Rand and its work from the vantage point of a twenty-fifth-year perspective. That is the burden of these remarks and of the excerpts and essays that follow.

Another purpose is to report on Rand's current activities, as we have done in years past. That report appears in Parts 3 through 6 of the volume.

By way of introduction, Rand is a California corporation, independent and nonprofit, consisting of about 1000 persons, headquartered in Santa Monica. Our purpose is research, and only that, on matters affecting the public interest—questions of U.S. strategic policy, for example; of the design, development, procurement, deployment, maintenance, and support of military forces; of urban development policies, and those involving education, health, housing, energy; and so on.

Rand has no stock or stockholders, no laboratories, no development or production facilities, no sales force, no product or services to sell in commercial or industrial markets. Our work is supported entirely by government agencies and private institutions concerned with public problems.

We have a resident professional staff of some 500 men and women—and an active program of hiring and advancing professional women, and members of ethnic and racial minorities. The resident staff is backed up by several hundred other professionals, mainly at university campuses, who work for Rand part-time as consultants. Rand has a current annual budget of about $30 million.

Our work draws upon most of the major disciplines in the physical, social, and natural sciences, along with engineering, mathematics, and computer science. The emphasis is more on application than on basic research in these fields; and the effort centers on problems of policy, planning, and development in military, domestic, and international affairs. The approach is analytic, systematic, and interdisciplinary.

Rand's sole output consists of research results, delivered to our sponsors in reports of various kinds. The large majority of this report output is made available also to the public, as described in Part 6 of this volume.

Rand is governed by a board of trustees who represent the public interest and are active in the affairs of the corporation. They oversee Rand's work, its fiscal operations, and its relationships with research sponsors. Trustees are listed in Part 4 of this book.

Rand exists because it does one thing well. Not invariably well, because it is in the nature of research to run the risk of being wrong. But Rand has built a reputation for quality research of a kind that can help government to serve the people. And the need is more acute today than it was when Rand was founded.

———————

Rand was conceived in the mid-1940s, as a way to continue the partnership between the nation's military leaders and its scientists who had contributed so much to ending the last war. The object was to prevent a next one.

Of course other institutions, in and outside of government, share the same antecedent. And yet Rand was unique. It was a social invention. It was in effect a halfway house, standing at the center of a triangle. At one vertex was government, a repository of very large problems and very large resources. At another stood the universities, a training ground and reservoir for the country's scientific talent. Industry, the nation's prime source of technology and engineering skill, occupied the third.

Rand was a meeting ground where problems and resources and science and technology came together. The institution was designed to facilitate that process:

- It was to be close to but independent of government. This would provide access to the people empowered to make decisions, and at the same time safeguard the research from the bias of agency doctrine and advocacy.

- It was to be nonprofit. That would facilitate Rand's access to sensitive and proprietary information and, even more important, avoid conflict in appearance as well as in fact between private interests and the public interest Rand was designed to serve.

- And it was to provide the environment and ambience of a university, both in its informality and in its commitment to intellectual independence.

Rand was incorporated in May 1948, with funding from The Ford Foundation, after a two-year gestation period as Project RAND—a special and experimental contract between the Army Air Forces and Douglas Aircraft Company. The Air Force Project RAND contract was transferred to The Rand Corporation in that year, and has been renewed without interruption to the present day.

———

Much has happened in the intervening years. A diversification in sponsorship began in 1950, when Rand undertook work for the Atomic Energy Commission in addition to the Air Force. In 1959 the Advanced Research Projects Agency of the Department of Defense and the National Aeronautics and Space Administration also became research sponsors.

The list of government clients further expanded in the early 1960s with the addition of other Department of Defense agencies, as well as the National Science Foundation, the National Institutes of Health, and the Agency for International Development in the Department of State.

A limited research effort on domestic issues started in the mid-1950s, as Rand researchers began to apply their experience and techniques to some of the serious and urgent problems arising in the civil sector of our society. This research picked up major momentum in the 1967-1968 period, for sponsors at the federal, state, and local levels.

Our most ambitious undertaking in the field of local government has been for the City of New York, which in 1967 invited Rand to develop with it a research program focused on some of the City's most urgent and complex problems. The progress made in this cooperative program during its first year led to the foundation in mid-1969 of a separate corporation—The New York City–Rand Institute—intended as a permanent center for the analysis of urban affairs, staffed by Rand, and governed by a board of trustees jointly selected by Rand and the City.

Beginning in the mid-1960s, growth in our Defense-sponsored research began to taper off. This was due in part to the impact of dollar ceilings imposed by the Congress on the amount of advisory research that the Defense Department could contract out. And it was due in part to a growing feeling in the Air Force that Rand had become insensitive to the needs and wishes of its primary sponsor.

The next several years in fact saw a reduction (from its peak period) of nearly 50 percent in the Air Force-sponsored portion of our national security work. Until 1968, however, this was offset by an increase in research sponsored by other Defense agencies, with the total level of effort in that research sector holding relatively constant at about 450 professionals. The total began to fall off in 1971, reaching a low point of about 250 professionals in 1972, where it has been stabilized for fiscal years 1973 and 1974.

During this same period our work in the domestic sector has been gradually expanding, and it now constitutes a program of nearly equivalent size.

And so in 1973, our 25th year, we find that Rand has come through a period of adjustment. We have a balanced research program. A little over half of our research staff is at work under federal sponsorship on problems of national security and international affairs; a little less than half is working on domestic affairs, for federal, state, local, and private sponsors; and a small number of staff, supported by Rand's own funds, is engaged in a variety of other research tasks in the public interest.

The current program of research is outlined in Part 3 of this volume.

———————

Much of the work of the past quarter-century was successful—some of it singularly so—because it clarified major policy issues, changed the attitudes and perspectives of public leaders, and influenced events in important ways. Or because it resulted in new ways of thinking about the problems of government and new methods for dealing analytically with them. Or because it brought about a synthesis of existing knowledge for application to new problems. Or simply because it added to the common fund of what is known about the world and how it operates.

The list is very long: research on an earth-circling satellite, Rand's first study, for example; on ballistic missiles and the strategic implications of nuclear weapons; on lunar flight; on structural materials, including titanium and beryllium, and structural fatigue; on strategic aircraft basing; on radar and communications, and reconnaissance systems; on computer science and technology; on R&D and logistics management; on the Russian and Chinese economies and bureaucracies, and the NATO alliance and the SEATO countries; on arms control and disarmament negotiations.

It also includes research on the economics of health care, the effectiveness of education, the provision of police and fire services; on housing and urban decay, data privacy, and transportation; and on the problems and prospects of cable television, and of energy supply. These are only a few examples of our work on substantive matters during those interim years—research that has made a difference.

But another aspect of our research was important throughout that period, and continues to be so today. That is the work of building the analytic tools to do the studies that make a difference. They were not all there when we started. And many of the modern ones are in widespread use today because Rand invented or developed them, and made them available through publication. They incorporate a practical philosophy for problem-solving—known in different contexts as systems analysis or the systems approach, or policy analysis—as well as a host of analytic techniques, both quantitative and qualitative, that allow the analyst to cope with problems marked by great uncertainty, competing alternatives, large costs, and far-reaching consequences. In the long run, it is this creative work on method that may be Rand's most lasting achievement.

In closing, it may be useful to reflect on some of the lessons we have learned as Rand begins its second quarter-century.

First, advisory research needs not only a competent producer, but a knowledgeable and sophisticated consumer. To get full measure, the consumer, or sponsor, must understand the long-lead-time character of policy-level research, and the distinction between answers and solutions. He must realize that research competence and wisdom are cumulative, that today's work on tomorrow's problems is likely to have deep roots in the past. He must, in short, have the vision and the patience—when he has the choice—to support long-term, broad-based research programs as a better strategy for solving problems than short-term, one-shot studies.

The sponsor must also understand that *finding out what needs to be studied* is a crucial part of the research process. This requires the closest interaction between researcher and sponsor from the outset, since the researcher must play a major role in selecting the most promising topics to explore and in defining the terms and limits of specific studies. Where the sponsor is able to maintain a qualified staff in house, the sponsor will contribute more to this study-formulation work—and will be aided in the evaluation of research results and in putting them to use.

It is important to success that relationships between sponsor and research organization be easy and familiar, but not so close as to encroach upon the organization's intellectual independence and hence upon its value to the sponsor as a source of objective advice.

It is important that the research institution be committed to the production of policy-relevant studies; that it be motivated by the prospect of public benefit; that it seek growth in quality, not quantity, in ideas, not in the number of staff members; that it bear the responsibility of staying with a problem, not merely writing a report and turning to a new concern. All of these things contribute to what, in the end, is the only thing that matters for an organization like Rand: its reputation for useful, high-quality research.

As we look to the future, we see no likelihood that the need will diminish for objective and systematic analysis of public policy issues. To the extent that Rand can provide such analysis, we will help society to see its choices before choices have to be made, and to understand the consequences of actions not yet taken. That could make the future better for all of us.

* * *

We dedicate this book to the men and women who created Rand; to those who helped it grow and flourish; to those at Rand today who work at seeing that it will continue to matter, tomorrow.

We reserve our special thanks to former chairmen of Rand's Board of Trustees: H. Rowan Gaither, Jr., William Webster, Frank Stanton, David A. Shepard, and Newton N. Minow; to Rand's past presidents Franklin R. Collbohm and Henry S. Rowen; and to all of the sponsors of Rand research, including in particular the remarkable institution that got it all started and supports a large share to this day, the United States Air Force.

Donald B. Rice
President

J. Paul Austin
Chairman of the Board

Contents

Sampler

Since its beginning, Rand has reported the results of its work in some 13,000 publications under its own imprint, in over 2000 articles published in professional journals, and in about 175 books produced by university and commercial publishers. Here we present a few excerpts from that body of work to indicate some of the concerns, present and past, of Rand research.

These excerpts do not reflect the portion of Rand's work that is either classified under Department of Defense security regulations (about 20 percent of the total) or so technical or mathematical as to be of immediate interest only to specialists. And we note that these passages, as well as the essays that follow, do not necessarily represent the official views or opinions of the sponsors of Rand research.

THE WORLD-CIRCLING SPACESHIP

Technology and experience have now reached the point where it is possible to design and construct craft which can penetrate the atmosphere and achieve sufficient velocity to become satellites of the earth. . . .

In this report, we have undertaken a conservative and realistic engineering appraisal of the possibilities of building a spaceship which will circle the earth as a satellite. The work has been based on our present state of technological advancement and has not included such possible future developments as atomic energy.

If a vehicle can be accelerated to a speed of about 17,000 miles per hour and aimed properly, it will revolve on a great circle path above the earth's atmosphere as a new satellite. The centrifugal force will just balance the pull of gravity. Such a vehicle will make a complete circuit of the earth in approximately one and a half hours. Of all the possible orbits, most of them will not pass over the same ground stations on successive circuits because the earth will turn about one-sixteenth of a turn under the orbit during each circuit. The equator is the only such repeating path and consequently is recommended for early attempts at establishing satellites so that a single set of telemetering stations may be used. . . .

In making the decision as to whether or not to undertake construction of such a craft now, it is not inappropriate to view our present situation as similar to that in airplanes prior to the flight of the Wright brothers. . . .

Though the crystal ball is cloudy, two things seem clear:

1. A satellite vehicle with appropriate instrumentation can be expected to be one of the most potent scientific tools of the Twentieth Century.
2. The achievement of a satellite craft by the United States would inflame the imagination of mankind, and would probably produce repercussions in the world comparable to the explosion of the atomic bomb.

Such a vehicle will undoubtedly prove to be of great military value. However, the present study was centered around a vehicle to be used in obtaining much-desired scientific information on cosmic rays, gravitation, geophysics, terrestrial magnetism, astronomy, meteorology, and properties of the upper atmosphere. . . .

. . . the primary cosmic rays could be studied without the complications which arise within the atmosphere. . . . Studies of gravitation with precision hitherto impossible may be made. . . . The variations in the earth's gravitational field over the face of the earth could be measured from a satellite. This would supply one very fundamental set of data needed by the geologists and geophysicists to understand the causes of mountain-building, etc. Similarly, the variations in the earth's magnetic field could be measured with a completeness and rapidity hitherto impossible.

The satellite laboratory could undertake comprehensive research at the low pressures of space. . . . A telescope of even modest size could, at a point outside the earth's atmosphere, make observations on [the moon, the sun, the planets, and certain nebulae] which would be superior to those now made with the largest terrestrial telescopes. . . . observations of the cloud patterns on the earth, and of their changes with time, could be made with great ease and convenience. . . .

The most fascinating aspect of successfully launching a satellite would be the pulse quickening stimulation it would give to considerations of interplanetary travel.

Excerpts from Preliminary Design of an Experimental World-Circling Spaceship, *Project RAND Report SM-11827, May 2, 1946. Although many scientists contributed to this study, these excerpts were written by Francis H. Clauser (Project RAND 1946-47), David T. Griggs (Project RAND 1946-48; Rand consultant 1948-), and Louis Ridenour (Project RAND 1946-48; Rand consultant 1948-50).*

MEDICAL COSTS, HEALTH INSURANCE, AND PUBLIC POLICY

Month after month medical care prices have been leading the consumer price index to new highs. Because of public reaction against these escalating costs, all levels of government have become involved with the problem of rising medical prices. . . .

In public debate about the causes of medical price rises, numerous villains have been identified. Fee-gouging physicians are commonly cited as a prime cause of rising prices. Others have assigned major responsibility to anarchy in the nation's hospital system. Also blamed are the drug companies, perennial scapegoats for high medical costs.

Actions and proposals to counter these causes of rising prices have been numerous. Demonstrators have appeared at the American Medical Association Convention to protest high fees, and proposals have been made to audit the tax returns of physicians who receive more than a certain amount from Medicare and Medicaid. Legislation has been proposed that would make individual hospitals subject to central planning authorities as a pre-condition for reimbursement from Medicare and Medicaid. Proposals for reducing the patent protection afforded drug companies have also been put forward.

Although the commonly cited causes may partially explain the rapidly rising price of medical care, the important role of increased demand for care has received relatively less public attention. Elementary economics teaches that if demand for a commodity increases and supply does not respond immediately, price will tend to increase. Particularly large increments to demand for medical care were caused by the Medicare and Medicaid programs. . . .

It is more than mere coincidence that the rise in medical prices accelerated sharply in fiscal year 1967, the first year of Medicare and Medicaid. Even before these programs came into existence, medical experts were complaining about shortages of skilled personnel, particularly physicians and nurses. Medicare and Medicaid added billions of dollars to the demand for medical care, thereby worsening the presumed manpower shortage and contributing to the upward pressures on medical prices.

... the percentage rise in hospital daily service charges has been approximately double the rise in physician prices and all medical care prices. In this paper we wish to consider the role insurance programs have played in contributing to price increases. Since the problem of rising prices appears most acute for hospital care, we will focus our attention there, but what we have to say applies to all medical services that are covered by insurance. ...

One of the important factors contributing to the rising demand for medical care has been the spread of medical insurance. Why should insurance affect demand? In effect, insurance lowers the price the consumer pays for consuming any particular medical care service. Many individuals believe that this should have little effect. They assume the consumption of medical care services does not respond to price (or to the provision of insurance). This view might be summed up by the statement: "If you're sick, you go to the doctor; if you're not sick, you don't." Most of the evidence we have contradicts this view.

The benefits of medical insurance, both public and private, are widely appreciated: Consumers are afforded protection against unpredictable requirements for large medical care expenditures; and the provision of government-sponsored insurance for low income persons is one means of eliminating financial barriers to medical care. ...

Joseph P. Newhouse (Rand 1968-; consultant 1967) and Vincent Taylor (Rand 1961-70; consultant 1970-72), Medical Costs, Health Insurance, and Public Policy, *Rand Paper P-4274-1, March 1970.*

THE ECONOMICS OF DEFENSE

The purpose of this book is to explain *a way of looking* at
military problems which we and others with whom we have
been associated have found fruitful in insights and productive
of solutions. Essentially we regard *all* military problems as, in
one of their aspects, economic problems in the efficient
allocation and use of resources. We believe that this way of
looking at military problems goes far toward reconciling the
apparent conflict of views between the officers and officials who
are responsible for defense and the officials and Congressmen
whose primary interest is economy—except in determining the
over-all size of the military budget, where conflict between
these points of view is inevitable. . . .

National security depends upon many factors . . . the morale of
a country's soldiers, the number and ingenuity of its scientists,
the character and skill of its political and military leaders, its
geographic position relative to other countries, and even—in
this nuclear age—the prevailing winds that blow across its
expanses.

But national security also depends upon economic factors,
which are variously interpreted and defined. Most speakers
and writers who stress the importance of economic factors are
referring to the economic strength of the nation, as contrasted
with its military forces. . . .

Other experts use the concept of economic factors more
narrowly, to refer to the constraints on military forces imposed
by the budget—the necessity to limit costs. . . .

In this book we will be concerned with economics in its more
general sense. Economics is not exclusively concerned . . . with
certain types of activities (industrial) rather than others
(military), or with the traditional points of view of budgeteers
and comptrollers. Being truly economical does not mean
scrimping—reducing expenditures no matter how important
the things to be bought. Nor does it mean implementing some
stated doctrine regardless of cost. Rather economics is
concerned with allocating resources—choosing doctrines and
techniques—so as to get the most out of available resources. To

economize in this sense may imply spending less on some things and more on others. But always economics or economizing means trying to make the most efficient use of the resources available in all activities in any circumstances. . . .

Economy and efficiency are two ways of looking at the same characteristic of an operation. . . .

For this reason it is misleading to imply . . . that economic or cost factors are necessarily in conflict with strategic, doctrinal, and technological considerations, and must somehow be reconciled with them, with not too much weight being assigned the economic. There *is* a conflict between defense and other goods in deciding on the size of the military budget. Economizing involves deciding how much of other things to sacrifice in the interests of military strength. But in all decisions on how to spend the military budget—on what kinds of equipment and forces, to implement what kind of strategy—there is no such conflict. Strategy, technology, and economy are not three independent "considerations" to be assigned appropriate weights, but interdependent elements of the same problem. Strategies are *ways of using* budgets or resources to achieve military objectives. Technology defines the *possible* strategies. The economic problem is to choose that strategy, including equipment and everything else necessary to implement it, which is most efficient (maximizes the attainment of the objective with the given resources) or economical (minimizes the cost of achieving the given objective)—the strategy which is most efficient also being the most economical. . . .

Charles J. Hitch (Rand 1948-61) and Roland N. McKean (Rand 1951-65; consultant 1965-66), The Economics of Defense in the Nuclear Age, *Harvard University Press, 1960, a Rand book.*

RACE DIFFERENCES IN INCOME

Some useful empirical studies have been done of relations between white and nonwhite income and some suggestive theoretical models of discrimination proposed. We have benefited from them. Nonetheless, not only the popular, but also the professional literature abounds in statements about the relations of nonwhite and white income distributions and their changes over time that do not seem to square with our own results. Sometimes the contradiction is only apparent, but more frequently it is genuine. It is sometimes said, for example, that the income gap between the races is greatest at the lowest levels of the income distribution. And there has been up until very recently a rather widespread impression of decline or stagnation, especially at the bottom. Such impressions have been common not only among militants but among moderate civil rights advocates; and not only among polemicists and politicians in ephemeral pamphlets ... [but] rather often in the writings of able economists and sociologists in the course of serious (and generally illuminating) studies. ...

Not all of these views are based on studies and some of the studies have been affected by rather severe limitations. For the most part:

1. Even where these writers talk of income distributions or make inferences that depend on the distributions, they have actually compared only medians or means; or where they have used distributions they have selected only a few points or used summary statistics (such as the Gini coefficient) that essentially enable comparisons only of inequality among nonwhites with inequality among whites, which is not the same as comparing inequalities in income between nonwhites and whites.

2. They have focused on one or a few income series—for example, family income or male income—and have sometimes drawn invalid inferences from these magnitudes to others—for example, total money income to persons.

3. They have sometimes drawn conclusions about personal income that really apply only to places or to job

categories—conclusions that do not apply to net figures covering both the starting and end point of migrations from one place or occupational category to another.

4. In estimating changes over time they have sometimes used rather short time spans, or pairs of years sharply affected by the cyclical variability of nonwhite absolute and relative income. . . .

The part of our study summarized here has compared white and nonwhite income along the entire distribution of each and developed several statistical measures and graphic devices for this purpose . . . estimated the effects on nonwhite relative income of differences in the distribution of whites and nonwhites by age, years of schooling, and major occupational categories . . . [and] explored briefly the relations to the data of various economic theories of discrimination in the marketplace, genetic explanations of income differences between whites and nonwhites, queuing models of the relative instability of nonwhite and white income during the business cycle, human capital theories of formal schooling and on-the-job-training as an investment process, a model of the dynamics of relative improvement in terms of migrations from one place, job category, or industry to a higher income place, job category, or industry. . . .

Although our study has been almost entirely concerned with income, this does not imply that we believe income disparities are the only important problem of race discrimination; nor that the only such problems of importance are economic; nor even that they are all quantifiable. But clearly a broad range of social, political, and economic problems is reflected in income disparities, and income data are among the most complete and tractable of the available quantitative measures. Moreover, income *is* important. Among other things, nonwhites do want more income, and more income relative to whites. . . .

Albert Wohlstetter (Rand 1953-63; consultant 1967-) and Sinclair Coleman (Rand 1968-), Race Differences in Income, *Rand Report R-578-OEO, October 1970.*

ARMS CONTROL: BUDGETS AND BUREAUCRACIES

The rationalistic approach to arms control, which dominates the public discussion, tends to rest upon speculation and syllogisms. It presupposes that arms decisions made by a rival are formulated by a national decisionmaking process, governed by something like a unified intelligence. There is, for example, a good deal of casual (one might say half-baked) speculation on what the Soviets might do; the resulting hypothesis is gradually transmuted into the certainty that this indeed is what the Soviets will do—with little attempt made to temper the speculation by considerations of bureaucratic or economic feasibility. The result is to impute tremendous flexibility to the Soviet posture. Little attention is paid to resource availability or to the deadening and stultifying effects of the bureaucratic process. Diabolically clever measures and countermeasures follow one another, and we are off into an ingenious—and, incidentally, a costless and frictionless—arms spiral.

By contrast, consider the real-world limitations on such a process. First, extraordinarily long lead times are encountered before a new weapon system is deployed and operational. Typically in public discussion these lead times tend to be ignored or truncated.... Nonetheless, one effect of sensibly introducing lead times is to stretch out the arms race. A second is that the weapons systems being designed today will be introduced a decade hence into what may be an altogether different strategic environment....

But there are other constraints, perhaps of greater importance, on a hypothetical arms race in which scientific marvels succeed scientific marvels. I almost entitled this paper "Budgets, Bureaucracies, and Blindness: The Three Hidden Weapons in Arms Control." It is these key ingredients that explain the slowness of arms responses, the lost opportunities, and the perseverance of vulnerabilities. Budgets after all are not unlimited, and major deployments, which in speculative design could occur simultaneously, compete for the same resources. For example, with limited budgets, it may be infeasible to project the expansion and upgrading of offensive forces at the same time that a major ABM deployment takes place. Moreover, for good bureaucratic reasons budgets, when limited, tend to be inflexible. Each bureaucratic element fights to preserve its fair share of the budget. New programs encounter resistance to obtaining ample funding. This bears on the issue of blindness, a term I use without pejorative intent since it is inherent in the human condition. Accepted doctrine tends sharply to limit permissible action and moderately limits permissible views. At any one time there is a somewhat stereotyped view of the threat, of proper strategy, and of acceptable armaments. Proposals falling outside of this circle, no matter how ingenious, encounter seemingly endless resistance before obtaining acceptance. . . .

In contrast to this *observed* sluggishness in changing military postures is a picture of rapid-pulsed technological revolutions presented by some weapons scientists and arms controllers. . . . One view suggests that the world will quickly be destroyed through an unfettered arms race unless political constraints are imposed that rein in technology. The opposite view suggests that an opponent will come into a position in which he can destroy U.S. retaliatory capacity and major cities in one surprise attack—unless U.S. technological advance is further stimulated. Nonetheless, there is an underlying similarity in the acceptance of the ease and speed of technological change.

My own conviction is that the use of rational models, presupposing quick perception, development, and absorption of new technologies and a high degree of interaction based on astute moves and countermoves, leads to a misunderstanding of the arms control problem. Nations, as they determine arms policies, should be viewed organizationally—as sluggish organisms, dominated by doctrines based specifically on obsolescent strategic views, and comprised of contending bureaucracies that create major obstacles to the instituting of serious change. Major changes come as a result of political shocks. . . . National powers of perception are quite limited—for large numbers of people must be persuaded that their previous judgments are outmoded. This is a time-consuming process at best. . . .

James R. Schlesinger (Rand 1963-69), Arms Interactions and Arms Control, *Rand Paper P-3881, September 1968.*

SYSTEM IMPACT ASSESSMENT: A COMPREHENSIVE APPROACH TO PUBLIC POLICY DECISIONS

Technology has advanced further in the twentieth century than in all previous history. But, like the Midas touch, this advance has been a mixed blessing. Many technological changes—supposedly advantageous—have brought not only their expected benefits, but also unexpected problems. These problems often have exceeded their benefits or have affected entirely different people, places, and parts of the environment. . . . For example, automobiles have multiplied personal mobility while contributing to air pollution, congestion, accidents, fuel shortages, and urban sprawl. . . .

Standard methods of analysis of policy alternatives have been largely preoccupied with quantifying everything in terms of dollars or some other single measure of effectiveness . . . to compare with the system cost. . . .

Furthermore, since a new transportation system, say, may bring travel timesavings to only the wealthy and noise impacts to only the poor, we must consider not just the aggregate impacts for a region, but also the *distributional impacts* —how the various benefits and disbenefits are distributed among different social groups.

Today, the growing complexity of society, the shortage of resources, and the strain on the environment make it imperative to assess proposed technological changes in terms of their *full range of impacts* on society and the environment, not merely in terms of direct cost and effectiveness. . . .

Several recent Rand studies have dealt with this problem in different areas. The technique they developed and used has been called *System Impact Assessment.*

This report uses a hypothetical decision . . . the best short-haul transportation system for the California region in 1985 . . . to illustrate how this approach includes all the effects and how it synthesizes and presents multiple attributes to a decisionmaker for comparison of alternatives.

The hypothetical alternatives considered are (1) the Base Case—the most probable 1985 system—with conventional aircraft, cars, and buses; (2) the VTOL case, with vertical takeoff and landing aircraft replacing the conventional ones; (3) the TACV case, with tracked air-cushion vehicles, which ride on a thin cushion of air on a concrete guideway, replacing conventional aircraft.

The many impacts—economic, financial, service, environmental, distributional—are estimated by special computer programs and then presented to the decisionmakers for comparison of alternatives. The usual approach combines the different impacts into a single measure of effectiveness. But this loses information and substitutes the analyst's values for those of the decisionmakers.

In system impact assessment, the various impacts are shown on a "scorecard" which shows, by color code, each system's ranking for a particular impact. The decisionmakers can then add to this factual knowledge their feeling for human values and those of the society they represent—the intangibles necessary for humane decisionmaking.

The following is a brief excerpt from a hypothetical scorecard showing a few of the many impacts (here in one color, with heaviest shading indicating the best system for a particular impact):

	Base Case	VTOL	TACV
Passengers (millions/yr)	7	4	9
Annual Subsidy ($ millions/yr)	0	0	90
Air Pollution (% all emissions)	3%	9%	1%
Percent of Noise-Impacted Households That Are Low Income	2%	16%	40%

Bruce F. Goeller (Rand 1964-), excerpts from a draft of a forthcoming Rand report.

WE HAVE PROVIDED THE SOUTH VIETNAMESE WITH A REPLICA OF THE AMERICAN ARMY

In all likelihood, the withdrawal of American forces from Vietnam will not end the war. Nor will our efforts to build up a large South Vietnamese army to replace our own forces guarantee the survival of South Vietnam.

We have provided the South Vietnamese with a replica of the American army; it is a formidable military machine, but, for economic and social reasons, South Vietnam *cannot* support it for very long, and the United States may not be *willing* to support it for the likely duration of the war.

Despite its strength on the battlefield, South Vietnam could fall. In fact, the danger that the country will collapse under the weight of its own military establishment may equal or even exceed the danger that it will be conquered militarily. . . .

As faith in conventional military methods and in the inexhaustibility of American resources diminishes while the prospect of continued war remains, many Vietnamese have begun to think about a different kind of an army to defend their country, one that is cheaper and less burdensome on the people, and might be more effective than the present cumbersome, conventionally structured, and overly Americanized army. They foresee South Vietnam's future defense force as a vast militia of armed peasants and part-time soldiers backed by a much smaller conventional army. This is hardly a new idea. In fact, it is probably close to the way the Vietnamese would have organized their own defenses if they had not been so imbued with French training and American military advice.

Coming from a wealthy country and accustomed to comparatively short wars fought overseas, Americans have had little experience with the problems that confront a small, poor country fighting a protracted war on its own territory. Long wars have been a regular feature of Vietnamese history. In often having faced that problem, the Vietnamese developed a number of techniques that enabled them to reduce the strain of sustained mobilization. We as advisors might do well to encourage the Vietnamese in their effort to apply some of these techniques, successful in Vietnamese history, to South Vietnam's present problems.

Changes are necessary, both in the composition of the armed forces and in the way they fight. This essay describes a concept of military organization and tactics that will be more tailored to South Vietnam's needs and capabilities than what it has now. It takes into account the limitations imposed by South Vietnam's economy, the possibility that American military assistance will be reduced, and the range of threats likely to be posed by the enemy.

South Vietnam faces a tenacious enemy that is determined to go on fighting. North Vietnam has not abandoned its objective of total victory. The Vietnamese have a tradition of long wars, and the North Vietnamese government has thus far shown itself more capable than the South Vietnamese government of imposing on its people the regimentation and austerity necessary to fight one. Members of the Hanoi government are themselves the survivors of thirty and forty years of struggle against the French and the Americans. They are not going to quit now, with the Americans withdrawing and with South Vietnam facing serious economic problems and in greater political disarray than usual. North Vietnam is unlikely to withdraw the 100,000 troops it maintains in South Vietnam or the more than 100,000 it maintains in Cambodia and Laos. Even if they cannot march on Saigon and take over the country, they keep South Vietnam under pressure and can exploit any signs of weakness. . . .

Brian M. Jenkins (Rand 1972-; consultant 1968-72), A People's Army for South Vietnam: A Vietnamese Solution, *Rand Report R-897-ARPA, November 1971.*

WELFARE AND FAIRNESS

New York State's Social Services Law requires each public welfare district to aid any person within its jurisdiction who is "in need of public assistance and care which he is unable to provide for himself." Presumably, the district must establish some objective standard by which a person's ability to provide for himself is evaluated; there must also be a standard of care to be provided to those eligible. The two standards may be the same.

Many groups have strong interests in the determination and administration of these standards. They include those who require public support, those who design and administer it, those who are concerned bystanders, and those who pay for it. The groups may overlap. Clearly, public policymaking must take into consideration the positions of all the actors; these positions may conflict both within and among the groups.

Under these circumstances, making any policy at all is difficult; making it "equitable," even more so. What is fair is, of course, a subjective judgment, influenced by an individual's philosophy and his perception of how he personally is affected.

But the problem of using equity as a criterion for evaluating welfare policies is deeper than that. What aspect of a policy should be tested for fairness? The principle by which it operates, or the results it produces? The impact on problems the policy addresses, or on those who pay, or one vis-à-vis the other?

Since equity may be defined in many ways, arguments on equity grounds can be mustered with equal justification for each of two opposing policies or on both sides of a single policy.

The welfare system in the United States is plagued by questions of equity that are increasingly commanding national attention. The cost of welfare immediately raises the question of who should pay. The participation of three levels of government in welfare administration results in policies of aid that differ among localities within a state as well as among states. The cost of living and taxation have narrowed the difference between the subsistence levels of aid granted to welfare recipients and the level of living open to the working poor. Whether or not they resolve these dilemmas "equitably," current proposals for a national system of welfare or family assistance are, to some extent, expressions of concern about these issues.

Of course, equity is not the only criterion by which welfare policies may be judged. Differing benefit levels are sometimes thought to encourage migration to high-benefit jurisdictions; providing high benefit levels for indigents may create disincentives for those able to work. Such social and economic consequences for society as a whole are also criteria by which welfare policies may be judged. Priorities among criteria are neither clear nor immutable.

Issues of equity are many and complex. Here we limit our discussion to problems of equity raised by DSS [Department of Social Services] housing policy, showing how current policy differentially affects households of equal "need." In the next chapter, we discuss the impacts of DSS housing policy on the behavior of welfare households, and of landlords. . . .

Ira S. Lowry (Rand 1963-), Judith M. Guéron (New York City Department of Social Services), and Karen M. Eisenstadt (Rand 1970-72; consultant 1972-73), Welfare Housing in New York City, *New York City–Rand Institute Report R-1164-NYC, November 1972.*

THE EMPTY-HOLE PROBLEM

The empty-silo problem (sometimes referred to as the empty-hole problem) . . . consists of determining [the probability] of residual missiles in [an enemy] silo complex from which some missile launches have been observed. . . .

MEMO (Model for Evaluating Missile Observation information), a computer model for evaluating missile-launch observation information, was developed as a tool to aid in solving the empty-silo problem.

[This] problem is essentially the following: Given the arrangement of a missile complex consisting of N silos, a set of k firings (k < N) from the complex, and a set of q observations (q = k for the model) of the firings by some sensor system, determine the unique *a posteriori* distribution of residual missiles in the complex.

MEMO simulates and analyzes the information gathered by an observation system viewing successive launches from a missile complex. Each launch is associated with one or several silos, depending on the quality of the information about the event. The model also computes certain statistics on the entire sequence of observations, as well as a first approximation to the distribution of the residual missiles.

Inputs to MEMO consist of the coordinates of each silo in the missile complex from some reference point . . . a method of selecting the missiles to be launched, and parameters describing the distribution of errors associated with the observation system.

The output data are arrayed in an observation matrix which has a row for each event (launch) and a column for each silo in the complex. The matrix has three different forms: (1) a display of the *distance* between each apparent launch point and the silos in the complex, (2) a display of the *likelihood* that a particular launch occurred from each silo, and (3) a display of the *probability* that each event originated from the various silos. . . .

Two versions of MEMO are presented, one written for the JOSS system ... an on-line, time-shared system developed at Rand ... and one written in Fortran IV....

Part 1 [of the JOSS program—the steps below numbered 1.01, 1.02 ...] inputs the initial information necessary to operate the program.... Part 2 generates a firing order either randomly or selectively.... Part 3 generates observations either randomly, selectively, or using the error terms from the previous run....

The [computer] program ... is given [below]:

1.01	Demand N as "Starting index value for sites".
1.02	Demand L as "Ending index".
1.021	Demand q(0) as "[Generating new or additional sites=1; otherwise=2]".
1.03	Do part 10 for i=N(1)L if q(0)=1.

. . .

2.01	Demand k as "number of firings".
2.012	Type "Invalid. Cannot be greater than No. of sites." if k>q(7).
2.013	To step 2.01 if k>q(7).

. . .

3.01	Demand j as "number of observations".
3.012	Type "Invalid. Cannot be greater than No. of firings." if j>k.

. . .

L. J. Pipes (Rand 1968-71; consultant 1971-), MEMO: A Model for Evaluating Missile Observation Information, *Rand Memorandum RM-6359-PR, July 1970. JOSS is a computing system developed at Rand that provides the individual researcher with his own personal computational service in his own working environment at relatively low cost. JOSS makes use of a simple, natural language.*

PROGRAM BUDGETING AND THE ANALYSIS
OF COSTS AND BENEFITS

In terms of the types of problems encountered in the total
program-budgeting process, one might think of a wide
spectrum going all the way from major allocative decisions on
the one hand to progress reporting and control on the other.
Major allocative decisions involve such questions as, Should
more resources be employed in national security in the future,
or in national health programs, or in preservation and
development of natural resources, etc.?

Ideally, the decisionmakers would like to plan to allocate
resources in the future so that for a given budget, for example,
the estimated marginal return (or utility) in each major area
of application would be equal. But this is more easily said than
done; and at the current state of analytical art, no one really
knows with any precision how the "grand optimum" might be
attained. In the main, the analytical tools now available
(particularly the quantitative ones) are just not very helpful in
dealing directly with such problems. Intuition and judgment
are paramount.

At the other end of the spectrum—progress reporting and
control—the main problem is to keep track of programs where
the major decisions have *already been made,* to try to detect
impending difficulties as programs are being implemented, and
to initiate remedial actions through a feedback mechanism
when programs are deemed likely to get out of control in the
future. Numerous techniques are available for dealing with
these types of program-management problems. . . .

The area between the ends of the spectrum is a broad and
varied one, offering the opportunity for applying a variety of
analytical techniques. These techniques are focused primarily
toward problem areas short of dealing with determination of
the "grand optimum," although they can be of real assistance
in sharpening the intuition and judgment of decisionmakers in
grappling with the very broad allocative questions.
Technically, this is called "suboptimization," and it is here
that the analytical efforts are likely to have the highest payoff.

... In that rare circumstance when a fairly complete set of calculations of cost and utility is possible and a resulting conclusion about a preferred alternative is reached, it may well be that the conclusion itself is not the most useful thing to the decisionmaker. For one thing ... the analysis usually cannot take everything into account—particularly some of the nebulous nonquantitative considerations. The decisionmaker has to allow for these himself. But more important, most high-level decisionmakers ... do not have time to structure a ... problem, think up the relevant alternatives ... trace out the key interactions ... etc. This the analyst, if he is competent, can do, and should do. And it is precisely this sort of contribution that may be most useful to the decisionmaker....

... let us be very clear about what is the main purpose of analysis in general, and cost-utility analysis in particular. Contrary to what some of the more enthusiastic advocates of quantitative analysis may think, we visualize cost-utility analysis as playing a somewhat modest, though very significant, role in the overall decisionmaking process. In reality, most major long-range-planning decision problems must ultimately be resolved primarily on the basis of intuition and judgment.

We suggest that the main role of analysis should be to try to *sharpen* this intuition and judgment. In practically no case should it be assumed that the results of the analysis will *make* the decision. The really interesting problems are just too difficult, and there are too many intangible (e.g., political, psychological, and sociological) considerations that cannot be taken into account in the analytical process....

In sum, the analytical process should be directed toward assisting the decisionmaker in such a way that (hopefully!) his intuition and judgment are better than they would be without the results of the analysis....

Gene H. Fisher (Rand 1951-), "The Role of Cost-Utility Analysis in Program Budgeting," chapter 3 in Program Budgeting: Program Analysis and the Federal Budget, *edited by David Novick (Rand 1949-71; consultant 1971-), Harvard University Press, 1965, a Rand book.*

WHY THIS BOOK ON CHINA POLICY
TURNED OUT AS IT DID

Our study started with a working hypothesis that did not quite survive. The hypothesis seemed reasonable enough. A great deal of work has been done on China by U.S. specialists since the Korean War. Had not our understanding of China outrun our policies? The work was begun, therefore, in the spirit of a search-and-rescue operation for insights and judgments widely shared among China specialists but not yet percolated through to the policymaking levels of the government.

Much searching was done, but few rescues were made. The United States has learned a lot about China, but our information is still swamped by the uncertainties that remain. The specialists disagree on a variety of important topics, the most important being Chinese intentions and perceptions.

No doubt this marks the beginning of wisdom. The United States certainly needs a more complex understanding of how the Chinese look at themselves, their history, and their relations with other nations. They do indeed see things differently than we do. But there is also great diversity among the Chinese themselves. We are just starting to understand their differences with each other. And those uncertainties compound the problems for the American specialist in forecasting the likely actions of China. Furthermore, much of what the specialist community does "know" is of little use to U.S. policymakers because it is not structured to fit the preoccupations of the policymaking level. The reasons for this are a major theme of the book.

On balance, we came to feel it probable that past U.S. policies were based on excessive fear of the aggressiveness of the Chinese Communists. Even this is uncertain because of the self-fulfilling nature of such policy premises. Especially since the Korean episode, apprehension and hostility on each side have stoked apprehension and hostility on the other. Justified or not, the self-fulfilling premises of the past become the realities of the present.

Even if our past notions of Chinese aggressiveness have been exaggerated, it is still uncertain what practical changes in policy would be implied. A conclusion as general as this does not automatically translate itself into concrete, workable policies. Judging from the recent increase in the flexibility of U.S. policy toward China, the Administration has reached a similar conclusion. Yet, it too is clearly having problems moving from a very general, still highly tentative conclusion to a forceful new policy stance.

Our quest for verities, therefore, turned into a study of how to make policy under conditions of great uncertainty. We propose two lines of attack. One has to do with increasing the policy relevance of what we do know or can find out about China through intelligence and research. But in the end, if the United States really wants to know more about China, it will have to go to the Chinese to find out. Our second approach, then, proposes exploratory policy moves toward China. Peking's responses (or lack of response) would help us learn more, and what we learned would then be incorporated into further studies and policies. In the course of time, it may be hoped, this process would substantiate (or dispel) our underlying premise, that better U.S.-China relations are possible. . . .

[This] study was drafted and organized to suit the concerns and working style of its target audience, high level policymakers and the community of China specialists within the government. These people have very little time. . . . Our study is therefore tersely argued. The language is often blunt. . . .

Richard Moorsteen (Rand 1956-67; consultant 1952-56, 1969-) and Morton Abramowitz (State Department), Remaking China Policy: U.S.–China Relations and Governmental Decisionmaking, *Harvard University Press, 1971, a Rand book.*

SOCIAL CHOICE AND INDIVIDUAL VALUES

In a capitalist democracy there are essentially two methods by which social choices can be made: voting, typically used to make "political" decisions, and the market mechanism, typically used to make "economic" decisions. . . . Elsewhere in the world, and even in smaller social units within the democracies, social decisions are sometimes made by single individuals or small groups and sometimes (more and more rarely in this modern world) by a widely encompassing set of traditional rules for making the social choice in any given situation, e.g., a religious code.

The last two methods of social choice, dictatorship and convention, have in their formal structure a certain definiteness absent from voting or the market mechanism. In ideal dictatorship there is but one will involved in choice, in an ideal society ruled by convention there is but the divine will or perhaps, by assumption, a common will of all individuals concerning social decisions, so in either case no conflict of individual wills is involved.

The methods of voting and the market, on the other hand, are methods of amalgamating the tastes of many individuals in the making of social choices. The methods of dictatorship and convention are, or can be, rational in the sense that any individual can be rational in his choices. Can such consistency be attributed to collective modes of choice, where the wills of many people are involved?

It should be emphasized here that the present study is concerned only with the formal aspects of the above question. That is, we ask if it is formally possible to construct a procedure for passing from a set of known individual tastes to a pattern of social decisionmaking, the procedure in question being required to satisfy certain natural conditions. An illustration of the problem is the following well-known "paradox of voting."

Suppose there is a community consisting of three voters, and this community must choose among three alternative modes of social action . . . [e.g.] no federal aid [to state education], federal aid to public schools only, and federal aid to both public and parochial schools. . . .

It is expected that choices of this type have to be made repeatedly, but sometimes not all of the three alternatives will be available. In analogy with the usual utility analysis of the individual consumer under conditions of constant wants and variable price-income situations, rational behavior on the part of the community would mean that the community orders the three alternatives according to its collective preferences once for all, and then chooses in any given case that alternative among those actually available which stands highest on this list.

A natural way of arriving at the collective preference scale would be to say that one alternative is preferred to another if a majority of the community prefer the first alternative to the second, i.e., would choose the first over the second if those were the only two alternatives.

Let A, B, and C be the three alternatives, and 1, 2, and 3 the three individuals. Suppose individual 1 prefers A to B and B to C (and therefore A to C), individual 2 prefers B to C and C to A (and therefore B to A), and individual 3 prefers C to A and A to B (and therefore C to B). Then a majority prefer A to B, and a majority prefer B to C. We may therefore say that the community prefers A to B and B to C.

If the community is to be regarded as behaving rationally, we are forced to say that A is preferred to C. But in fact a majority of the community prefer C to A. So the method just outlined for passing from individual to collective tastes fails to satisfy the condition of rationality, as we ordinarily understand it. Can we find other methods of aggregating individual tastes which imply rational behavior on the part of the community and which will be satisfactory in other ways? . . .

Kenneth J. Arrow (Rand consultant 1948-), Social Choice and Individual Values, *Rand Memorandum RM-291-PR, July 1949; also published as a Cowles Commission Monograph (John Wiley & Sons, 1951).*

UNCONTROLLED AND PURPOSELESS VIOLENCE

Before 1914 the wars to which civilized governments resorted were somehow, with a few exceptions, limited in their potentialities for evil. War had always been violent, but only rarely had the violence been uncontrolled and purposeless. . . .

The first World War proved, and the second one confirmed, that the twentieth century not only had put into the hands of each great nation a war machine of far greater power than any known before, but also had seen a near-collapse of the factors previously serving to limit war, including that of common prudence. In the course of World War I, the original cause of the outbreak and the initial purpose with which each belligerent had entered the quarrel were forgotten. The war created its own objectives and stimulated commitments among the allies that made it practically impossible to end the conflict short of the collapse of either side. . . .

World War I was the purposeless war, which no one seemed to know how to prevent and which, once begun, no one seemed to know how to stop. The world it brought in its wake has been politically a much worse place than it was before. If the second World War enhanced the power of the great communist state, the first World War created it and also gave rise to the corruptions of Fascism and Nazism.

World War I was also a war which, because of technological changes of much lesser degree than those which are new to us now, completely baffled the military leaders who had to fight it. They were not incompetent men, but they had been reared under a regime of maxims and precepts which bore no relation to the situation in which they found themselves. Their ability to make reasonable deductions from the events in which they were caught up seemed to be paralyzed by the very magnitude of those events. It was such a situation as Clausewitz had described where "man, who in great things as well as in small usually acts more on particular prevailing ideas and emotions than according to strictly logical conclusions, is hardly conscious of his confusion, onesidedness, and inconsistency." Their bafflement and confusion contributed enormously to the tragedy. For while all major wars are bound to be costly in lives and wealth, World War I proved that it makes a great deal of difference how they are fought....

It must be asked: What were these men after that they were willing to pay so high a price for it? Strangely, this question has rarely been asked in all the years that have since passed. The high commands of both sides in World War I have often been condemned for their methods, as well as for their arrogance, insensibility, and what not, but almost never for their lack of objective! Clearly, each side was trying to achieve "victory." But what did that mean? It is abundantly evident that for the commands of both sides the term was a mere symbol, almost devoid of content save that it determined who asked whom for an armistice. In a very literal sense it concerned simply the question of who was to cry "uncle!" ...

There is no reason to suppose that the politicians were any more clear-headed than the soldiers about the goals towards which they had been driving their peoples and their armies. For them too the symbol of "victory" was self-sufficient....

Thus it was possible for great nations to proceed to battle with an energy previously undreamed of, and almost no sense of direction. "Events," as Churchill put it, "passed very largely outside the scope of conscious choice. Governments and individuals conformed to the rhythm of the tragedy, and swayed and staggered forward in helpless violence, slaughtering and squandering on ever-increasing scales, till injuries were wrought to the structure of human society which a century will not efface, and which may conceivably prove fatal to the present civilization...."

Let us remember about the soldiers of World War I that it was their horizons rather than their skills which proved so disastrously limited. They were confident they had the right answers. And there is nothing in the stars that guarantees our own generation against comparable errors....

Bernard Brodie (Rand 1961-66; consultant 1949-51, 1969-),
Strategy in the Missile Age, *Princeton University Press, 1959, a Rand book.*

CITIZEN PARTICIPATION IN PLANNING
CABLE TELEVISION

Many cable entrepreneurs view urban cable television as a potentially massive new market, to be tapped somewhat in the same fashion as were the older, rural markets. That is, the cable system will provide excellent reception and a wide selection of television channels, and will enlist subscribers on this basis.

Such a view of urban cable television neglects two important developments. First, advanced urban cable systems can offer much more than cable television has been able to offer in the past. Through its multiplicity of channels (upwards of 20), its ability to reach specific audiences, and eventual two-way interaction, urban cable will bring not only a greater variety of television programs, but new forms of urban communication. Over cable, community centers can interact with City Hall, community meetings can be televised, individual citizens can discuss their interests with experts in special fields, and people could even do their shopping. Such innovations raise problems and issues far different from those in traditional cable television systems.

Second, cable's entrance into urban markets comes at a time when urban citizens are keenly aware of the advantages—and threats—of new technology as applied to the city. Citizens in many cities are also more highly organized and more articulate than ever before. This means they will keep a watchful eye on the development of any cable system in their cities and especially in their neighborhoods. They will press for assurance that the services they want are provided, and possibly that control of the cable system remains with some local and public-minded group, not with a distant, private entrepreneur.

These two new developments intensify the necessity for careful planning of urban cable systems. With the general rise of participation in municipal affairs, citizens are sure to demand a voice in the planning process; and municipal officials can turn their interest to advantage in designing a system that will be responsive to public needs and preferences. Naturally, citizen participation also entails risks, not the least of which may be prolonged delay or even stoppage of the whole project. . . .

Urban citizens *will not accept* a passive role. . . . They may even feel unintimidated by the expertise held by study groups, franchise applicants, or other recognized cable "experts." As residents have learned through their experiences in other large-scale public programs, active citizen participation in the planning process is a necessary prelude to any subsequent citizen responsibility in helping to design, operate, or use cable systems. Moreover, citizen participation that begins only with the public hearings on cable franchises may be too late to be effective. By that time, many options already may have been eliminated. Instead, the public will want to make its desires known during the initial study period, when it can shape the very questions that are to be asked, and not merely offer alternative answers to narrowly conceived questions. . . .

In addition to new entertainment, the new urban cable systems promise to provide citizen access to television programming and such new public services as fire and burglar alarm systems, new health and social services, at-home adult education, and neighborhood-specific services. These services will be more client-oriented, and hence perhaps more effectively delivered, if the citizens who are their potential users have participated in the design and planning stages. . . .

The call for citizen participation in the development of cable television, and especially in its planning, comes from the recognition that urban cable development will occur within the broader context of recent events in the American city. These events have included consistently greater citizen involvement and control over activities affecting the city. . . .

Robert K. Yin (New York City–Rand Institute, 1970-72; Rand, Washington, 1972-), Cable Television: Citizen Participation in Planning, *Rand Report R-1136-NSF, March 1973.*

THERE IS THE TARGET!

In many operations, success depends on a human observer's finding quickly a certain object in a scene or in some image of that scene.

In Air Force operations, armed reconnaissance and many kinds of strike missions depend critically on the timely identification of a target (or its image) by an airborne observer. Whether he is observing directly with his unaided vision, using optical aids, or viewing the display produced by an intervening sensor (e.g., television, radar, or any other imaging transducer), the same capabilities for visual search, discrimination, and recognition are involved.

No matter how complex or sophisticated the sensor in front of him or the computer and other mechanisms behind him (e.g., for measuring coordinates or rates or for aiming weapons), the most crucial—and least understood—step in the whole operation is his conscious decision that "There is the target!"

The purpose of this Memorandum is to propose a model that describes analytically the performance of a human observer in such a task as a function of a number of well-defined and measurable parameters.

While no subjective act can be analyzed completely, the kind of situation described in the above paragraph is one in which the usually cited sources of variability and unpredictability in human behavior are minimized. By contrast, the task of monitoring an empty scene or display—waiting for something to happen—would be extremely difficult to model because the observer is so quickly subject to boredom and to "wandering" of an otherwise unoccupied mind.

But the present case requires active search in a structured field for a known (or briefed) specific object, or perhaps for any of a class of familiar objects, such as trucks on a road. In either case, the task is carried out for a fairly short period of time under conditions of very strong motivation. Under such circumstances, the variability in individual performance and the difficulty in specifying that performance may well be less than the variability between scenes and the difficulty in quantitatively describing the content and the degree of congestion in typical pieces of terrain. . . .

This Memorandum presents a model for describing analytically the capabilities and limitations of a human observer in the task of looking for and finding known or expected fixed objects. . . . The model is structured according to three distinguishable psycho-physical processes: deliberate search over a fairly well-defined area, detection of contrasts (a subconscious retino-neural process), and recognition of shapes outlined by the contrast contours (a conscious decision based on comparison with memory). In addition, when the observer is viewing a displayed image of a scene, noise is usually present which degrades his performance of these three steps. The probability that the three steps are completed successfully, multiplied by a noise degradation factor, gives the probability of target recognition $[P_R = P_1 \times P_2 \times P_3 \times n]$.

A search term $[P_1]$ expresses the probability of looking in the right direction for the target as a function of the desired search rate . . . and a measure of scene congestion or false-target density. . . .

[The search term] P_1 is the probability that an observer, searching an area that is known to contain a target, looks for a specified glimpse time (viz, 1/3 sec) in the direction of the target with his foveal vision. P_1 is a function of the ratio of an acceptable search rate to that demanded in a given situation; the loosely defined concept of foveal vision is replaced by that of an effective glimpse aperture. . . .

H. H. Bailey (Rand 1953-), Target Detection through Visual Recognition: A Quantitative Model, *Rand Memorandum RM-6158/1-PR, February 1970.*

GAMES AND SCIENCE

... the body of Game [Theory] doctrine now in existence is not even able to cope with full-blown real games; rather, we are restricted at present to very simple real games, and to watered-down versions of complicated ones, such as Poker.

It may be baffling then that someone devotes valuable energy to the study and development of Game Theory—and, moreover, expects you to participate! The reason it is done is in part an act of hope and of faith, stemming from past successes. For the invention of deliberately oversimplified theories is one of the major techniques of science, particularly of the 'exact' sciences, which make extensive use of mathematical analysis....

Mathematics has been called many things. Among others, the queen of sciences and the handmaiden of the sciences. Therefore, while there seems to be some doubt regarding its precise social position, there is general agreement regarding its gender. In fact, all sciences probably look pretty feminine to the men who attend them: They obviously find the work desperately attractive, and the history of scientific investigation is full of evidence that she whom they court is changeable and capricious; in short, something of a hussy.

Moreover, the way she responds to a push, or to guidance, is usually astonishing. She moves freely, but frequently in an unexpected direction. Time and again men have spent their lives trying to move her in a specified direction, quite without success. Viewed narrowly, their work would be classed as a failure. But, since science usually moves somewhere when pushed, these failures often are the bases of completely unexpected successes in other fields....

J. D. Williams (Rand 1946-64), The Compleat Strategyst, Being a Primer on the Theory of Games of Strategy, *McGraw-Hill, 1954, a Rand book.*

... Это тем более вероятно, что существующая в настоящее время теория игр не в состоянии справиться с реальными развлекательными играми без их упрощений. Поэтому мы ограничены сегодня областью очень простых реальных игр и выхолощенных версий таких сложных игр, как покер.

Может показаться странным, что кто-то расходует драгоценную энергию на изучение и развитие теории игр, да еще хочет и вас вовлечь в это дело! Причиной этих занятий теорией игр являются надежда и вера, которые мы черпаем из успехов, имевших место в прошлом. Ведь разработка искусственно упрощенных теорий является одним из важнейших научных методов, особенно в так называемых точных науках, широко использующих математический анализ....

Математике дают самые различные имена. Часто ее называют королевой и служанкой наук. Хотя иногда высказываются сомнения относительно ее точного социального положения, не возникает никаких разногласий относительно ее пола. Действительно, любая наука, по всей вероятности, предстает в облике прелестной женщины для тех, кто занимается ею. Они считают свою работу чрезвычайно привлекательной, и история научных исследований полна доказательств изменчивости и капризности той, которой они служили.

Более того, ее реакция на попытки подталкивания и руководства является обычно совершенно ошеломляющей. Она движется свободно, но зачастую совершенно в неожиданном направлении. Очень часто люди проводят всю жизнь, пытаясь продвинуть ее в определенном направлении, но безуспешно. С узкой точки зрения их труд можно было бы считать неудачей. Но так как наука все же движется в каком-то направлении, когда ее подталкивают, эти неудачи часто являются основой для совершенно неожиданных успехов в других областях знания....

From the Russian edition of *The Compleat Strategyst,* 1960.

CUBA AND PEARL HARBOR: HINDSIGHT
AND FORESIGHT

Before both the Pearl Harbor attack and the Cuban missile
crisis, intelligence had provided the American government
with lots of information on the approaching crises. But in both
cases, regardless of what the Monday morning quarterbacks
have to say, the data were ambiguous and incomplete. There
was never a single, definitive signal that said, "Get ready, get
set, go!" but rather a number of signals which, when put
together, tended to crystallize suspicion.

The true signals were always embedded in the noise or
irrelevance of false ones. Some of this noise was created
deliberately by our adversaries, some arose by chance, and
some we made ourselves. In addition, our adversary was
interested in suppressing the signs of his intent and did what
he could to keep his movements quiet.

In both cases the element of time also played against us.
There were delays between the time information came in, was
checked for accuracy, evaluated for its meaning, and made the
basis for appropriate action. Many of these delays were only
prudent, given the ambiguities and risks of response.

The interpretation of data depends on many things, including
our estimate of the adversary and of his willingness to take
risks. This depends on what our opponent thinks the risks are,
which in turn depends on his interpretation of us.

We underestimated the risks that the Japanese were willing
to take in 1941, and the risks that Khrushchev was willing to
take in the summer and fall of 1962. Both the Japanese and
the Russians, for their part, underestimated our ultimate
willingness to respond. . . .

It is important to understand that the difficulties described are
intrinsic, that they are examples of a much wider problem in
the confrontation of any body of knowledge with the
deliverances of experience. By focusing on mis-estimated
capabilities, dispositions, and intentions, we obscure the fact
that, without a very large complex body of assumptions and
estimates, the data collected would not speak to us at all. . . .

The complex inferences involved in the act of interpreting photographs are made possible only by a large body of assumptions of varying degrees of uncertainty, ranging from principles of optics and Euclidean geometry through technological, economic and political judgments. The inferences from the interpretations themselves in turn are based on an even wider range of uncertain beliefs. . . . Some of the relevant assumptions may be held passionately. They are likely to include wishful or self-flattering beliefs, items of national pride or claims at issue in partisan debate. . . .

Our expectations and prior hypotheses guide our observations and affect their interpretation. It is this prior frame of mind, now changed, that we forget most easily in retrospect. And it is this above all that makes every past surprise nearly unintelligible—and inexplicable except perhaps as criminal folly or conspiracy. . . .

After the event, of course, we know—like the detective story reader who turns to the last page first, we find it easy to pick out the clues. And a close look at the historiography of Pearl Harbor suggests that in most accounts, memories of the noise and background confusion have faded most quickly, leaving the actual signals of the crisis standing out in bold relief, stark and preternaturally clear. . . .

We cannot guarantee foresight, but we can improve the chance of acting on signals in time and in a manner calculated to moderate or avert a disaster. We can do this by a more thorough and sophisticated analysis of observations, by making more explicit and flexible the framework of assumptions into which we must fit new observations, and by refining, and making more selective, the range of responses we prepare so that our response may fit the ambiguities of our information and minimize the risks both of error and inaction.

Roberta Wohlstetter (Rand 1948-65; consultant 1965-), Cuba and Pearl Harbor: Hindsight and Foresight, *Rand Memorandum RM-4328-ISA, April 1965.*

ESTUARY MODELS: RIVERS, TIDES, AND COMPUTERS

The largest parts of the population of the United States are very close to the major estuaries along the East and West Coasts. It can be expected that the population in these metropolitan areas will increase. As these estuaries are, in many cases, the only open spaces close to these metropolises, very heavy pressure is brought to bear to develop them.

The importance of navigation projects will diminish in relation to other objectives such as preservation and improvement of health standards and water quality, conservation, expansion of airports, sanitary landfills, building of causeways, and providing of hurricane barriers and "mining" of fill to combat beach erosion.

This shifting emphasis, together with a tremendous increase in the complexity of our problems, renders past experience and methodologies far less certain guides. The typical approach consisting of the benefit-to-cost ratio of a particular project becomes increasingly more difficult to determine ... [for] economic analysis of a particular project is not generally done in the context of a larger system.

We will be forced to start to manage our estuaries, select the objectives we want to obtain, and make plans that best fit these objectives within the limits of resources of the estuary, investment capital, aesthetics, and political, legal, and administrative constraints, taking into account the risks involved....

Development along the estuaries will be more and more under control, particularly from the point of view of water and air pollution....

In our management of estuaries and the adjacent sea, the tidal flow of water is of the utmost importance [for] relatively small changes may have marked effects.

It has been typical in the United States to study tidal flow with comprehensive physical models....

These aids have served well, but modern management techniques require data in manageable form which can be processed on computers. For example, the time has passed when we want to look only at so-called flushing characteristics of tidal estuaries. Now, systematic analyses need to be made of maximum benefits of water pollution control facilities by investigating the location of outfalls, degree of treatment, and releases of storage reservoirs for flow augmentation during periods of minimum flow. We also now need to include biochemical processes, bacteria deposition by sedimentation, aeration at the surface, and the effects of heat, to mention a few. . . .

It is this writer's opinion that the development of mathematical models for tidal flow and estuary problems lags five to ten years behind the progress that has been obtained in modeling atmospheric fluid flow, ocean circulation, and shock hydrodynamics. . . .

The model's representational ability now has the potential to exceed in clarity the visual representation obtained by hydraulic models; active displays can be made on cathode ray tubes. The mathematical model becomes a digital simulation model, where changes can be made by simple tracing of input curves on a [Rand] tablet. . . .

The development of digital simulation models is time-consuming but highly rewarding. . . .

Jan Leendertse (Rand 1961-), Discussion—"New Horizons in the Field of Tidal Hydraulics," *Rand Paper P-4106, June 1969, describing his computer analysis of the flow of coastal and estuarine waters. This work was begun for the Air Force in a study of the damage that might be produced by a nuclear explosion in water. The work has since been extended to include, for example, problems of water pollution, and has been applied to the Rhine estuary, Jamaica Bay, and elsewhere.*

THE POLITICS OF VICTORY AND DEFEAT

Allied strategy in World War II was dominated by the concept of surrender. In the Western belligerent countries, both the leaders and the populations took it for granted that the enemy's final defeat would take the shape of mass surrender of his forces.

In most earlier wars of the modern era, the image of surrender did not play a similar role in strategic thinking; there were other suggestive images of the victorious termination of wars, such as the "battle of annihilation" or the conquest of the enemy's capital, followed by the dictation of peace terms. . . .

The armistice accord that concluded hostilities in World War I was indeed in the nature of a final mass surrender, but the strategy that led to it emerged only gradually by trial and error, and the terms imposing capitulation came as a surprise. It was only in World War II that surrender, and unconditional surrender at that, was adopted in advance as the final objective of one side. . . .

It is not sufficient . . . to look at surrender only from the military point of view. Acts of surrender do more than liquidate military operations; they initiate new, nonviolent cycles of mutual dealings between winners and losers. Surrender as a goal concept, therefore, serves to shape ideas of the political relations between states after the termination of hostilities. . . .

The American policymakers were desperately anxious to hasten Japan's surrender and to cut terminal costs as much as possible, but their basic concept of nonnegotiation ruled out the one form of political strategy that was best suited to saving time. . . . In this way, one of the basic corollaries of the unconditional surrender policy, nonnegotiation, interfered with the speedy liquidation of the war.

The other corollary of the policy, nonrecognition of the enemy government as the legitimate custodian of national sovereignty, also caused difficulties. . . .

The United States acted as if the problem were that of defeating Japan, when in fact the problem was to avoid an unnecessary last battle *after* Japan was defeated. . . .

Some uncertainty, of course, is always involved in estimating at any given time whether strategic victory has been achieved or whether the enemy acknowledges his strategic defeat and is ready to act accordingly. The Allies' terminal policy toward Japan, however, did not go astray because of faulty intelligence on these points. Its basic flaw was, rather, a defect of doctrine. All terminal resistance whatsoever was regarded as necessarily incompatible with the enemy's awareness of his strategic defeat. . . .

Not only does this fundamental error prevent the winner from doing what the terminal situation requires; it also warps his strategic plans by inducing him to treat the question of strategic victory as an open one when it no longer is so. This is what happened during the last stage of the Pacific war, with disastrous consequences. Impressed by the strength of Japan's residual capabilities, the United States came to the conclusion that Russian help was needed to "defeat" Japan. . . .

The fact that the preferred method for forcing Japan into surrender was that of stepping up destructive warfare reflects the same misconception. That method culminated in the dropping of the atomic bombs, an act that constituted a heavy moral liability for the United States and that, as now seems certain, made no essential contribution to Japan's surrender without a last battle. The American government, of course, could not know at that time what we know now, and those who made the decision were convinced that many lives, American as well as Japanese, would be saved by it. But this conviction would not have prevailed if the nature of the problem of obtaining surrender, as distinct from that of achieving defeat and impressing this fact on the enemy, had been clearly realized. . . .

Paul Kecskemeti (Rand 1948-66; consultant 1966-70), Strategic Surrender: The Politics of Victory and Defeat, *Stanford University Press, 1958, a Rand book.*

CLOSED CIRCUIT TV FOR THE PARTIALLY SIGHTED

Rand ... has been working for the past six years on the
design, fabrication, and informal testing of closed circuit TV
(CCTV) systems for the partially sighted. These instruments
permit a large fraction of the legally blind population, as well
as persons who have severe visual impairment, to read printed
and handwritten material, to write with a pen or pencil, and
to carry out other operations that require precise eye-hand
coordination. Over the past two years, more than 120 partially
sighted people have tried out our CCTV systems. They ranged
in age from 5 to 90 and had a wide variety of eye disorders,
including macular degeneration, retinitis pigmentosa, optic
nerve atrophy, and diabetic retinopathy. *Many of these people
are unable to read printed or handwritten material or to write
with a pen or pencil without the aid of a CCTV system.*

The exact number of legally blind people in America is not
known. However, based on available data, we have concluded
that they number about 400,000. . . . We estimate that at least
60 percent of them have enough residual vision to benefit from
the use of a CCTV system. In addition, about a million literate
Americans are unable to read a newspaper even with the aid
of eyeglasses. . . . [Estimating that] 600,000 of the latter
population who are not legally blind could benefit from a
CCTV system, we may conclude that over 800,000 Americans
could benefit from such a device. . . .

[Closed circuit TV systems are now] helping partially sighted
people of all ages. For example, they permit students to read
the pages of a book, take notes, write reports, or do
mathematics, allowing people of working age to compete for
jobs that until recently have been closed to them because of
their limited eyesight. (Such devices permit them to read
plans, study diagrams, examine ledgers, make notes, and write
reports.) CCTV systems are also enabling the elderly to read,
write, and sew long after their vision has become so poor that
they are unable to carry on these enjoyable activities with
their unaided eyes or even with eyeglasses.

Many partially sighted people, who are unable to read or
write even with the aid of eyeglasses, are very concerned with

their inability to read personal mail, to examine bills, and to write checks without the help of a sighted person. Their inability to carry out such activities unassisted implies a loss of privacy and independence that irks them. Properly designed CCTV systems are enabling many of them to carry on these important day-to-day functions in complete privacy....

One of the primary reasons that a CCTV system proves so useful to the partially sighted is that it is an image enhancement device. This means that the signal received by the TV camera can be electronically manipulated ... to produce a magnified image on the monitor screen that is brighter and has greater contrast than the object being viewed by the TV camera....

... in fact, the contrast can even be reversed from black on white to white on black, if desired.... This is particularly valuable to partially sighted people who are bothered by scattered light, for example, persons who have scarring on the cornea, lens opacities, or light-scattering material floating in either the anterior or posterior chambers of the eye....

Proposed future research ... [includes among] its objectives a general survey of opportunities for developing electro-optical devices to aid the partially sighted in obtaining education and employment, and in performing certain other activities that are of importance to them but that are currently beyond their capability or can be handled by them only with excessive expenditures of time and energy.... In addition ... the functional problems of the partially sighted should be structured in a way that suggests feasible types of prosthetic instruments for alleviating these problems....

Samuel M. Genensky (Rand 1958-), Harold E. Petersen (Rand 1966-70 and 1973-; consultant 1970-73), Hubert L. Moshin (Rand 1954-), Raymond W. Clewett (Rand 1951-), and Roy I. Yoshimura (Rand 1955-), Advances in Closed Circuit TV Systems for the Partially Sighted, *Rand Report R-1040-HEW/RC, April 1972.*

THE EXPERT'S ROLE IN POLICYMAKING: RATIONAL ANALYSIS, MUDDLING THROUGH, AND THE CLINICAL APPROACH

Discussions of the strengths and weaknesses of program budgeting and systems analysis have often taken the form of an argument between those who point out the merits of bargaining or "muddling through"—in its most explicit formulation, Lindblom's "disjointed incrementalism"—as an approach to policy formulation in a democratic society and those who sing the praises of rational analysis and systematic planning.

While the differences between the two approaches are important and interesting, there are no grounds for all-out battle. It is not a matter of one versus the other, since the two are more complementary than mutually exclusive. Each can be a help to the other in certain situations.

Some of us might like to see systems analysis have more influence in the policymaking process and politics and bargaining somewhat less, but most people—if pushed a little—would agree that each has its place.

That still leaves two questions: (1) What is the place of each? and (2) What is the most fruitful way for the two—bargaining and analysis—to interact? The latter question really becomes, "How should systems analysis relate itself to the political and bargaining aspects of policy formulation?" since systems analysis is still the weaker one and it will adjust to politics more than vice versa.

There is another set of problems in policymaking that neither systems analysis nor incrementalism has much to say about. . . .

There are many areas within government agencies and other organizations where we all think they could do much better than they are now doing. Without any analysis, most of us could point to examples of too little coordination between programs, redundant programs or procedures, use of clearly inefficient techniques, little use of available information, underutilized personnel, etc.

We all think we know about such things, especially in someone else's organization, but few of us have prescriptions for dealing with them effectively.

These are organizational problems or people problems. Incrementalists tend to consider them as political problems with a small "p" and to handle them in the same terms as large "p" politics. . . . Systems analysts have tended to ignore them, or to grumble about them, or, more recently, to fit them into a rationalistic model.

Both approaches regard this set of problems as more or less insoluble. To the extent they prescribe to the analyst, they suggest how to live with organizational problems not how to improve organizations. . . .

The third approach . . . places organizational problems at the center of its concerns. Its objective is to build or, more accurately, to grow better organizations. . . .

All three approaches—systems analysis, incrementalism, and the clinical approach . . . see the environment of the policy agency . . . as messy and chaotic and each has to figure out some way of making the analyst's task manageable. Where they differ is in their solutions to this manageability problem. Systems analysis squarely faces the challenge of the inhospitable analytic environment and attempts to create some semblance of order *useful for action purposes.* . . . Incrementalism, on the other hand, absolves the analyst of much of the worry by assuring him that politics can serve as a sort of putty plugging up the holes in his analysis. . . .

The clinical expert ignores the messiness of the world; instead he attempts to service the client so that the client is better able to cope with it. . . .

Kathleen A. Archibald (Rand 1967-71; consultant 1971-), Three Views of the Expert's Role in Policy-Making: Systems Analysis, Incrementalism and the Clinical Approach, *Rand Paper P-4292, January 1970.*

AIR FORCE SPACE MISSIONS AND COMPUTERS

Most military space operations during the 1970s will not strain the available information-processing capabilities. But there are some operations—real-time image processing, multisensor data analysis, decision-oriented displays, and others—for which the Air Force will not be able to reach "on the shelf" and find tools capable of doing the job.

The USAF will have to settle for reduced capabilities in these areas, unless space-mission planners more thoroughly investigate their detailed information processing requirements and couple them more effectively to the USAF R&D program in information processing. . . .

The proposed Space Transportation System (STS) . . . or space shuttle . . . *will* strain the available information processing capabilities. Historical data on similar software projects indicate that six or seven calendar years are probably required to design, develop, and check out the software for a project of the magnitude and complexity of STS.

To make sure that software does not slip the overall schedule, STS planners must begin to design the software *now*. Also, the USAF should push R&D on high-capability flight computers for STS.

Preprogrammed space software in the seventies will allow many more user options. Serious consideration is being given to "programmer-astronauts" and real-time software modification to provide non-preprogrammed flexibility to USAF space-mission operations.

But, coupled with our inadequate capabilities to check out and certify software, such measures could have disastrous consequences in escalating strategic crises or degrading critical defense capabilities because of undetected errors in software options or modifications. . . .

Software certification is not easy. Ideally, it means checking all possible logical paths through a program; there may be a great many of these. For example, [in one very] simple program flowchart . . . the number of different paths is about ten to the twentieth. If one had a computer that could check out one path per nanosecond, and had started to check out the program at the beginning of the Christian era (1 A.D.), the job would be about half done at the present time.

So, how does one certify a complex computer program that has incredibly more possible paths than this simple example? Fortunately, almost all of the probability mass in most programs goes into a relatively small number of paths that can be checked out.

But the unchecked paths still have some probability of occurring. And, even in the most thoroughly checked systems, software errors can occur. . . .

On Apollo 8, an unforeseen sequence of astronaut actions destroyed the contents of a word in the computer's erasable memory—fortunately, not a critical error in this case. And on Apollo 11, the data flow from the rendezvous radar was not diverted during the critical lunar landing sequence, causing a computer overload that required Astronaut Armstrong to divert his attention from the process of landing the spacecraft—fortunately, again, without serious consequences.

Computer support of some military space missions will be at least as complex as that of Apollo, with two additional factors that will render the software certification problem even more difficult. First, the military systems will be far less organized about achieving a single objective; second, they will rarely have as much time to check out program modifications. . . .

Barry W. Boehm (Rand 1959-73), Some Information Processing Implications of Air Force Space Missions: 1970-1980, *Rand Memorandum RM-6213-PR, January 1970.*

REMOTELY MANNED SYSTEMS IN TACTICAL AERIAL WARFARE

By every measure, Remotely Manned Vehicles (RMVs) will prove more versatile, more accurate and much less costly than conventionally operated tactical aircraft—they mean a new era in air warfare....

Three fundamental factors force the interest we now see in possible military uses of RMVs: *the increasing lethality of antiaircraft defenses,* the present level of vehicle and equipment *costs,* and the *technological advances* of the past ten years or so, especially in electronic and avionic equipment....

Over a period of three years, World War II air operations in Europe cost some 40,000 aircraft and about 160,000 air-crew members, both nearly equally divided between U.S. and U.K. forces.... Translated to present aircraft costs, the bill for vehicles alone would come to nearly $200 billion....

Clearly we face a growing problem in tactical aerial operations (and, one suspects, analogous ones for the many other kinds of operations): *How to improve accuracy—which has the most important influence—in the face of ever better air defenses, while decreasing costs and air-crew losses?*

In brief, we must spend fewer dollars per target "hit" and incur fewer losses per target attacked. We need cheaper vehicles, and we need to keep people out of the line of fire. We must simultaneously find a way to stand off from thick defenses at targets and achieve better accuracy. Unfortunately, the most successful way yet discovered to achieve the necessary accuracy is well known—*get close to the target.*

Thinking along these lines, you may ask the following question: If we must or want to use an air vehicle, why do we have to have man *in* it? How much of the time, during what fraction of a combat sortie, does a man *really* count? It does not seem too much to say that it's only for a few seconds or a few minutes during a combat sortie that he does. We can arrange to take off, land, and fly the airplane routinely without him. We really only need him when he, in effect, has to *"see"* something—*discriminate* and *decide.* And these three functions are the very ones that we had not been able to build machines to do at all well. The other functions—flying, steering, taking off, landing, navigating—we can and have built machines to do.

Now, as it happens we have the technical means to displace these three functions too—by communications and clever remote control. . . . All the necessary parts for remotely manned tactical aircraft turn out to be developed in practical, economical form. Perhaps the most significant advance has been the successful development of the remotely controlled electro-optical auto-tracking seeker. . . .

To make an RMV cost-effective, the designer must exercise great care in selecting and developing component parts or subsystems . . . [and must] specify *no more performance than really will be necessary* for any specific operation. . . .

The discriminating aeronautical engineer . . . selecting new construction methods and new materials, should be able to reduce typical airframe cost in an RMV by as much as two-thirds, while maintaining approximately the same vehicle weight and adequate performance. . . .

Although both development and production costs of current large turbine engines for manned aircraft are notoriously high, and development is somewhat risky, this need not be the case for RMV engines. . . .

William B. Graham (Rand 1950-), Remotely Manned Systems in Tactical Aerial Warfare, *Rand Paper P-4768, June 1972. This paper was published as the cover story of the May 1972 issue of* Astronautics & Aeronautics. *It has been reproduced by Rand with the permission of the publisher.*

COMMUNIST CHINA ENTERS THE NUCLEAR ERA

Since the establishment of the Peking regime, China's overriding objectives have been the preservation of her national security, the achievement of independent great power status, and the filling out of her territorial boundaries in Taiwan and Tibet. None of these objectives could be realized unless China was militarily strong—a proposition that had become vastly complicated in the nuclear age.

Could military power, in its modern sense, be achieved without the appropriate economic and scientific foundation? . . .

Or was it imperative that China concentrate the major part of her resources on economic development on the assumption that only a broadly based development of her industrial production capabilities would open the way for her scientific and technological advance, and thus create the foundation for an enhanced defense posture in the future? This study has primarily concerned itself with the manner in which the Chinese sought to resolve this problem. . . .

The very years during which the Chinese Communists were gaining and consolidating their power on the mainland were marked by nothing less than a revolution in weaponry and strategic doctrine beyond China's borders. Yet for a few years after 1949 there was little to indicate that the new regime was aware it had emerged into a nuclear environment in which an enemy might in theory destroy its cities, industrial complexes, communication centers, and transportation facilities by air attack with nuclear weapons. . . .

A long look at the course of Communist China's foreign and military policies since 1949 reveals that two major shifts in Chinese foreign policy have coincided closely with major developments in Soviet military thought and weaponry. China's adoption in 1954 of a policy of peaceful coexistence in relation to her Asian neighbors occurred shortly after the initiation in the Soviet Union of a debate on the implications of nuclear weapons for modern warfare.

Similarly, China's apparent loss of interest in peaceful coexistence and her more bellicose political approach to Asia followed within a matter of months the Soviet Union's testing of an intercontinental ballistic missile and launching of earth satellites in the second half of 1957. . . .

To the decision-makers in Peking, the Soviet technological-military breakthrough in the second half of 1957 must have appeared to signal the end of a period during which the combined requirements of China's internal economic program and the external balance of power seriously reduced the range of techniques available to her for affecting the international scene. The shift in the balance of forces, which they confidently believed had occurred, was now expected to provide them with new and more flexible areas for political and military maneuvering behind the shield of Soviet nuclear power. . . .

Thus, Peking's evaluation of Soviet military-technical developments provides the key to China's more bellicose attitude in late 1957 and, at the same time, to China's apparently frustrating relationship with the Soviet Union since then. . . .

However, China probably considers her present external posture a temporary one, and stands ready to exploit more vigorously her political and military power as soon as she detonates a nuclear device and moves progressively toward acquiring a nuclear capability. Depending on the extent of Soviet assistance, China may be expected to detonate her first nuclear device some time in the 1962-63 time period and within a few years thereafter to have produced a limited nuclear stockpile. . . .

Alice L. Hsieh (Rand 1959-1969; consultant 1955-58),
Communist China's Strategy in the Nuclear Era, *Prentice-Hall, 1962, a Rand book.*

COMPUTERS AND CANCER

It seems certain that in the next thirty years—by the year 2001—the computer will become a major instrument in support of clinical practice. Part of our task today is to look beyond the frustrations, expense, and apparent waste of our present prototype systems and to distinguish the important themes which will bind medicine and computers together.

In computer medicine we are clearly in the exploratory phase of a new technology—a position analogous to the early designers and users of automobiles. With the introduction of the automobile came a great variety of expensive, made-to-order cars which could only be run on poorly maintained muddy roads. To drive required a large measure of patience, enthusiasm, and self-reliance, coupled with a fine sense of the ridiculous. Moreover, the automobile scared the horses, and otherwise challenged the established order of things. . . .

This is a talk about mathematical modeling, simulation, and leukemia chemotherapy; but I have opened in this way because it is not the details of leukemia chemotherapy which I want to emphasize, but rather the far-reaching changes which information processing is destined to bring to this field. The primary changes will be found in the conventions of clinical decisionmaking.

The use of mathematical modeling and the computer in leukemia chemotherapy is particularly illustrative of a new form of medical practice because (1) the untreated disease is usually rapidly fatal and deserves the investment; there are 14,000 new cases a year, many in children and young people; (2) it is quantifiable; the leukemia cells can be sampled in the blood and the bone marrow; (3) it responds to rational, well-organized therapeutic regimens; effective drug doses and schedules can be set up which depend upon cell kinetics (models of cell behavior) and pharmacokinetics (models of drug distribution); (4) the impact of drug therapy is quantifiable; thus the regimens can be evaluated and the models verified; and (5) good results depend upon a persistent, well-organized approach.

We might put the argument another way: We have strong drugs with which to treat leukemia, but our therapeutic advantage is sufficiently small, and our knowledge sufficiently limited, that the penalty for sloppy thinking and sloppy patient management is particularly high. This disease is a test of our ability to manage medical information, to understand its implications, and to apply our knowledge wisely. Because quantitative data are the key aspect of decisionmaking in this disease, skill in the use of quantitative information is essential to success.

At the same time, because of the importance of teamwork between the specialties of hematology, clinical oncology, infectious disease, and laboratory medicine, leukemia therapy is an excellent test of the ability of computer technology to coordinate the relevant information. Moreover, success, short of a cure, requires long-term sophisticated maintenance therapy, and thus effective long-term records. . . .

As a physician working in this field, I can only present my experience with the hope that it offers some generality. To build my models, I have been using BIOMOD, a Rand-developed software package designed specifically for on-line interactive model building and simulation. It provides a data tablet, keyboard, and full graphics capability with a resolution of 1024 by 1024. The system has the capacity to enter models in mathematical formats so that the computer does the machine-language programming and can produce, compile, and run a new program in a matter of minutes. The system can keep track of 20 output curves and display five of these on command. As a simulation progresses, the evolving curves are presented on the screen. The scale of the graphic output can be changed interactively and the displayed variable combined and redefined. The simulations can contain up to 20 modifiable parameters so that the simulation can be stopped, parameter values changed, and then allowed to proceed. . . .

Thomas L. Lincoln, M.D. (Rand 1967-), The Clinical Significance of Simulation and Modeling in Leukemia Chemotherapy, *Rand Paper P-4775, March 1972.*

A NEW GENERATION OF LEADERS
IN LATIN AMERICA

Latin America has been governed in recent decades by local political elites who were philosophically allied with the United States or who frequently responded to U.S. pressures and cues even when they were not in ideological agreement. These elites ranged from the extreme-right to the democratic-left. . . .

Though frequently differing with Washington on some issues, these leaders nevertheless tended to align themselves initially with the United States on major global questions or to respond ultimately to U.S. inducements and pressures. Hence, the Latin American governments supported the United States on such vital Cold War issues as internal communist subversion, relations with the Soviet bloc, and admission of China to the United Nations. During the 1960s, moreover, they joined with the United States in isolating Castro's Cuba and in repelling the *fidelista* guerrilla and Soviet strategic threats to the hemisphere. . . .

Several developments suggest that the characteristic susceptibility of Latin America to U.S. blandishments may already be lessened. . . . Reformist and even militantly leftist wings developed within the Church—once considered the bastion of conservatism and oligarchical privileges—in Brazil, Peru, Chile, and other countries. New political parties with modernizing social and economic perspectives, like the Christian Democrats in Chile and Venezuela, succeeded in winning power from established parties. . . .

These changes have had direct consequences for governmental actions, frequently in novel directions. The Panamanian military government in power since 1968 has repeatedly reaffirmed Panama's total sovereignty over the Canal Zone. After seizing power in October 1968, Peru's nationalist and developmentalist military regime moved swiftly in carrying out structural reforms affecting foreign and domestic capital, while two years later Chile's duly elected socialist coalition government began implementing the "peaceful road to socialism. . . ."

Latin American leaders currently seem to perceive fewer internal and international constraints on their actions, and therefore tend to be more innovative than were most of their predecessors. Despite their many differences, for example, Peruvian military and Chilean socialist regimes share the common attributes of assertive nationalism, economic developmentalism, and social reformism.

We believe these characteristics typify a leadership style likely to predominate during the 1970s among what we might call a new "political generation" assuming positions of power and influence. . . .

Unlike the radical left as well as anti-communist politicians of the 1960s, however, this emergent generation of leaders will probably be more eclectic in choosing among alternative diplomatic, political, and economic formulas. They are as likely to reject the indiscriminate adoption of the Soviet or Cuban models of communism as they are certain to resist the wholesale emulation of the American way of life for their societies. In particular, Latin American nationalists are drawing on the negative as well as positive lessons to be gained from the *fidelista* experience in Cuba. . . .

Though less extreme than the *fidelista* leadership, the new generation of leaders may nevertheless be as taxing for U.S. policy as was Cuba during the 1960s. In the 1970s, Latin American elites seem certain to move toward reducing their countries' patterns of dependency by seeking to exploit new opportunities in the changing international environment. . . .

Edward Gonzalez (Rand consultant 1969-) and Luigi R. Einaudi (Rand 1962-), "The New Leadership Generation," a chapter in Latin America in the 1970s, *edited by Luigi R. Einaudi, Rand Report R-1067-DOS, December 1972.*

THE NATIONAL INSTITUTE OF EDUCATION: PRELIMINARY PLAN

American education faces severe problems.... The expansion of educational opportunity has occurred unequally, bypassing many children born into social or economic disadvantage. Even the more privileged too often find education at all levels joyless, inappropriate, or ineffective. Educational institutions, from school districts to universities, face severe financial crises. Yet even where sufficient resources are available, too little is known to assure their effective use....

But the aspirations are high as well; Americans continue to expect much from their educational system. It should convey to members of the coming generation the knowledge and values of the previous one; develop in them the capacity to increase knowledge and strengthen values; and inspire among them the will to use that knowledge in the service of their values. It should prepare its students to adapt to life half a century into the future, in an age when fifty years spans several technological and social millenia, and offer them the opportunity to renew their skills and themselves throughout their lives. It should equip its graduates to be effective contributors to society, to be intelligent consumers, to be wise voters, and to be understanding parents.

And it should do all this for children of poverty and neglect, as well as for those of comfort and care, while the vocational needs of the economy are changing, society's structure and values are shifting, technology and science are reshaping the physical world, and the fund of knowledge to be conveyed is building at an ever-expanding rate. The aspirations are high indeed.

To alleviate its problems and achieve its aspirations, *American education, at all levels and in all forms, must undertake a continuous program of improvement and reform.*

... we do not know enough about how to design new forms of education; train and select educational personnel more effectively; reshape institutions so that they become more flexible and responsive; develop and introduce contemporary curricula into the schools; or make instruction at all levels more personal and adaptive. Nor do we know enough about how to obtain the funds essential to change; overcome resistance to useful change; develop agents of change; or provide the best current knowledge to those who need it to bring about change. *Lack of knowledge is a major impediment to achieving improvement and reform of American education....*

The President proposed creation of the National Institute of Education in his *Message on Education Reform* of 3 March 1970. He described it as "a focus for educational research and experimentation in the United States. When fully developed, the Institute would be an important element in the nation's educational system, overseeing the annual expenditure of as much as a quarter of a billion dollars." At the same time, the Department of Health, Education, and Welfare submitted legislation to authorize creation of the NIE....

There is considerable agreement among the several proposals for a National Institute (or Institutes) of Education on various features: location within the Department of HEW; separation from the Office of Education (OE); conduct as well as support of development, in addition to research; and concern with the problems facing American education. There is possible disagreement on whether the NIE should be singular or plural when it begins.

But an even larger set of questions exists on which there is neither agreement nor disagreement, since the proposals have not explicitly attempted to answer them: How shall the Institute(s) be internally organized? ...

Roger E. Levien (Rand 1960-; consultant 1956-60), National Institute of Education: Preliminary Plan for the Proposed Institute, *Rand Report R-657-HEW, February 1971.*

SOVIET OBJECTIVES AND STRATEGIES
IN THE SEVENTIES

How will the political and military conditions of the seventies shape Soviet objectives and strategies?

Soviet objectives will remain in the seventies as they were in the past, subordinate to the first objective of the Politburo—Soviet security and whatever it deems an essential component of it. This objective embraces, more especially, the integrity of Soviet borders, the adhesion of the Eastern European states, the defense of the Party, and the strength of its armed forces.

These first priority security objectives are, naturally, largely defensive in character. But the Soviet strategic and political position is too powerful to confine her to a Soviet "fortress" posture and especially so since, as the historical record shows, the Politburo esteems highly the value of buffer zones and of a "forward" or offensive posture, an appreciation that strategic parity with the United States will enable her to indulge more freely. That this is so should not lead one to forget what her top priority requirements are. A person who is well-to-do may show little day-to-day concern with basic necessities, but it would be a mistake to ignore their top priority status. Czechoslovakia, 1968, illustrates this point.

In the seventies the Soviets may be inclined to expand the list of political and military "necessities," and for the following reason—the growth of Chinese power and the possibility of an alliance of U.S. (Western) nuclear and technical capabilities with Chinese manpower....

The possibility is difficult for Americans to absorb that the Soviet Union may no longer consider the United States her most *dangerous* enemy, although certainly her *strongest* enemy. As the present decade wears on, Soviet preoccupation with China will probably grow, a preoccupation that nuclear parity/superiority is not likely to erase. The Soviets no longer seem committed to the belief that the United States and the West are waiting to annihilate them if opportunity permits, although they probably do not view this as an irreversible state of affairs. In any event, Soviet parity/superiority combined with the political climate of the Western nuclear powers assures the Soviets as well as can be expected for the foreseeable future of the deterrence of the United States and Western Europe.

In evaluating where their greatest hazards lie, the nuclear superiority of the United States over China may not be for the Soviets the most relevant aspect of the situation. What may well concern them more is that they are going to have to balance Chinese manpower superiority with a nuclear superiority that eventually may be stalemated by Chinese nuclear forces. They may thus find themselves in the position of the West when it relied on a (diminishing) nuclear superiority to balance Soviet conventional forces.

It is not likely that the Russians will derive much long-range comfort from the reflection that they are also still superior to China in conventional warfare capabilities. Perhaps it might be easier for the United States to understand the Soviet position if we think of ourselves as having to deal with Soviet military power *while at the same time* facing a Red China located where Canada now is.

Soviet leaders, like most European political leaders, generally have a longer time perspective and shape policy with longer future periods in mind than is customary in the United States. To say that the Soviets are preoccupied with China is not, therefore, to say that they expect imminent war or all-out war in some indeterminate future. Nor does it even mean that they exclude the possibility of a cautious rapprochement. But their strategic planning will surely increasingly take into account that they face two very different potential enemies on two very different and geographically separated fronts. In the absence of major changes, Soviet political and military planning in the seventies will probably lean heavily on the supposition of neutralization of the West and a more uncertain future in the East....

Herbert Goldhamer (Rand 1948-72; consultant 1972-), The Soviet Union in a Period of Strategic Parity, *Rand Report R-889-PR, November 1971.*

JUPITER-ORBITING SPACE MISSIONS: GRAVITY ASSIST FROM JUPITER'S MOONS

The energy and direction of motion of a space vehicle can be changed significantly by a close encounter with a moving gravitational body. This fact suggests that a spacecraft making a hyperbolic approach to a planet might use the gravitational attraction of a planetary moon in order to transfer to an elliptical orbit about that planet without expending fuel.

This study investigates the use of the four large moons of Jupiter to effect the capture of a spacecraft by Jupiter....

Many gravity-assisted trajectories have been suggested which use the close approach of an intermediate planet to perturb a trajectory going between the earth and a target planet. Considerable savings in fuel and/or time can result from using such a trajectory. In fact, a proposed gravity-assisted mission passes by Jupiter, Saturn, Uranus, and Neptune and requires only 8.9 years to complete, while a direct flight to Neptune requires 30 years.

A logical extension of this technique is to use a flyby of a planet's moon(s) to effect capture of the vehicle by the planet. The earth, Jupiter, Saturn, and Neptune all have sizable moons.

Two missions for the not too distant future might use moon flybys:

1. Because Jupiter is the nearest of the large planets, flights whose objective is to go into orbit around the planet would certainly be of great interest. Jupiter is extremely massive—in fact, more massive than all the other planets combined—which indicates that the fuel required to enter a low-altitude orbit is considerable. Among its many moons there are four massive ones with diameters comparable to that of Mercury and masses up to one-half that of Mercury. A flyby of one of these moons might not only decrease the minimum propulsion requirements significantly but would also afford observation of the moon itself.

2. Round-trip flights from the earth to Mars might fly by the earth's moon on the return leg of the journey in order to minimize the overall fuel requirements. Also, swingbys of the earth's moon to increase a space vehicle's energy might be used on many outward-bound interplanetary trajectories.

However, the large sensitivity of the resulting trajectories to initial launch errors must be weighed against the fuel savings. . . .

The purpose of this study is to investigate the usefulness of the moons of Jupiter in effecting capture of a spacecraft. A simplified model is used to approximate the maximum possible energy change as a function of the approach energy for each of the four large moons. If the energy change is sufficient to decrease the space vehicle's energy below the zero parabolic energy level, capture is accomplished. The sensitivity of the energy change to variations in the angle of approach and the distance of closest approach to the moon is also investigated, but little attention is given to the trajectories required to obtain the energy change.

None of these results in a final circular orbit, but because of the large energy decrease required to orbit at low altitudes, the most desirable final orbit is considered to be highly elliptic to afford close observation of the planet at pericenter without requiring too large an energy loss. Perturbations of the final orbit due to the presence of other moons have been ignored, as have any constraints due to possible radiation belts. Perturbations due to other moons can, of course, be minimized by introducing some velocity component out of the moon's orbital plane during the swingby. . . .

R. W. Longman (Rand consultant 1966-69), Gravity Assist from Jupiter's Moons for Jupiter-Orbiting Space Missions, *Rand Memorandum RM-5479-PR, December 1968.*

TRAINS FASTER THAN AIRPLANES

The Very High Speed Transit or "VHST" concept was put forward some years ago in response to the search for a pollution-free transport method that could operate at speeds competitive with aircraft. The general principles are relatively straightforward: electromagnetically levitated and propelled cars in an evacuated tunnel.

The VHST is predicated as an addition to the future transportation scene and will offer not only a fast and convenient transit method but also a tunnel complex to house utility transmission and auxiliary freight-carrying systems. . . .

The VHST is designed to connect directly with local systems. It is visualized that a passenger steps off a subway (or a people-mover from an auto parking facility) and gets on a VHST vehicle in the same terminal.

The VHST's "tubecraft" ride on, and are driven by, electromagnetic (EM) waves much as a surfboard rides the ocean's waves. The EM waves are generated by pulsed or by oscillating currents in electrical conductors that form the "roadbed" structure in the evacuated "tubeway." Opposing magnetic fields in the vehicle are generated by means of a loop of superconducting cable carrying on the order of a million amperes of current.

The system is highly conservative of energy. The tubetrain is accelerated to its maximum velocity, coasts for a brief period, and then is decelerated. Nearly all the power goes into kinetic energy; in accelerating, it employs the energy of the surrounding EM fields, but like trolley cars of the past, in decelerating, it returns this energy to the system. Its optimized electrical drive system is quite efficient, and further, it does not have to squander unrecoverable energy in climbing to high altitudes, as does an aircraft.

What sort of speeds are needed and how might these be achieved? Speeds as high as 14,000 mph have been examined in studies by . . . Rand . . . (in an example case of a direct link between Los Angeles and New York requiring 21 minutes transit time). The speeds required will certainly be on the order of thousands of miles per hour on the long-haul links. . . .

Transportation systems pose well-known problems to the environment. The bitter controversy over the sonic booms of the SST has perhaps obscured some other environmental effects of the SST—and aircraft in general. None of the energy required to levitate and propel the aircraft is recoverable; it all goes into the atmosphere along with combustion products. Long-term buildup of these products in the upper atmosphere is a matter of concern, and is a process that we are just beginning to understand. As aircraft become faster, airports must become more remote and operating altitudes higher, both aspects contributing further to environmental problems.

The use of a tubetrain would alleviate these hazards to the environment. . . . Right-of-way costs, surface congestion, grade separation problems, and noise pollution would be eliminated.

Sharing of facilities could help pay the high cost of such tunnels. Included among these contemplated underground systems are pipelines for oil, water, gas, waste disposal, and slurries of material such as coal and other bulk commodities; communication links, including channels for lasers and microwave waveguides; electrical power transmission lines such as superconducting cables; and passenger and freight-hauling systems.

Superconducting power cables will require a controlled environment to protect the cryogenic refrigeration system that makes superconduction feasible. A controlled-access tunnel is a virtual necessity for such a system. This type of power cable will alleviate many of the problems of siting of future power stations, since they can be located at great distances from the user and yet suffer negligible power losses in transmission. . . .

Robert M. Salter (Rand 1948-54, 1968-; consultant 1954-55, 1965-66), The Very High Speed Transit System, *Rand Paper P-4874, August 1972.*

Essays

In these short papers, all but two of them written especially for this volume, members of the Rand staff discuss their current research interests from individual perspectives. The topics exemplify subject areas in which Rand has already produced significant research, and which are likely to be important elements of our research agenda in the future.

2

Changes in schooling aimed at providing education are correctly perceived not as reforms, but as social revolutions....

John Pincus

Education, Schooling, and Civilization

For millenia, education has been considered a civilizing influence on mankind. In modern times, education is identified with schooling, and this has led to some confusion about their social roles. Schooling takes up more and more of people's time, but there is no convincing evidence that people are better educated or societies more civilized than they were long ago. The spread of schooling has served primarily to equip people for their social and economic roles in a complex society, rather than to further their education.

Educational philosophers from Plato to Dewey have thought of education as a lifelong process, not necessarily associated with any particular institutions of schooling. Many writers have thought of compulsory state-sponsored schooling as inimical to education, because it serves the purposes of the state rather than the needs of the individual. Some recent writers have suggested that the contemporary school is so chained to mindless routine that society would benefit from its abolition, with teaching and learning becoming the responsibility of individuals to each other. Others would retain the schools, while transforming them to allow for far greater contact with the rest of the social system, in the form of apprenticeship, broadly defined. Another variant would restrict schools' functions to custody and skill training, while reserving education, defined as the teaching of values and appropriate modes of conduct, to the family.

In historical perspective, it is clear that education is not the same as schooling, and its outcome is measured differently. The measure of our education is how civilized we are as individuals and social animals. The common measures of our schooling are years in attendance, the level of the schools' academic standards, and our performance there according to those standards. The links between civilization and the quantity or quality of schooling are unclear. Standards and aspirations for civilization change. The oligarchic societies of ancient and recent times associated civilization with the culture of the nobility and of the cities, where only a tiny fraction of the people lived. Moreover, most city dwellers supported the civilization of their era, but did not participate. "I am a Roman citizen" was a statement long reserved for very few.

Today, almost everywhere, this older concept is repugnant. For well-known reasons, reflecting the interaction of politics and technology as well as the power of the ideas of justice, progress, and equality, an ever-increasing fraction of citizens in all countries claim equality of opportunity and of treatment before social institutions—the law, the economic system, the educational system, even the once-unbridgeable barriers of social class and sexual and racial privilege.

Just as there have been many ideas about who should participate in the mainstream of a culture, so there have been many definitions of civilization. Today no civilized person would avow a preference for owning slaves or torturing his enemies; for most of history, great civilizations did both. Hundreds of years ago civilized men practiced codes of chivalry under a vision of civilization that we now term quixotic, after the characterization of the greatest satirist of those codes.

The idea of a civilized society, however, has in some ways changed very little over the millenia. It is one that encourages people to base their behavior on reason, moderation, consideration of others, and toleration of a wide range of opinions; and to develop, as they are able, both understanding and aesthetic appreciation. Two things have changed: the relative number of people who are classified as worthy of consideration by those who participate in the culture; and the forms of dogma, defined as issues that admit of very little toleration.

In medieval Europe, dogma was the domain of the church, which regulated the conduct of business between mortal men and their immortal souls according to unchallengeable norms. In the modern world, dogma is the domain of national states, which offer for the faithful their several political ideals, visions of felicity on earth, each according to unchallengeable norms. In both cases, toleration of the unfaithful is held to demonstrate a want of civilization, and even of elementary decency, not deserving of consideration by civilized folk.

Because education, and the aspirations for civilization that it implies, was long the domain of the upper classes, it was closely associated with wealth and with schooling, a luxury that the working classes could not afford and the state would not subsidize, at least until the growth of complex economic systems made it necessary to create a skilled labor force. Because of the correlation among education, wealth, and schooling, people began to believe that in order to become educated and wealthy, it was necessary to go to school. The implicit view held by a great many people in industrial societies is that people who attend school for a long time are educated, and educated people are rich—or at least comfortable and respected. Therefore, if you want to get rich, go to school and get an education.

In fact, the association is correlative but not entirely causative. Recent research has shown that in contemporary America there is an imperfect relationship between income and schooling. But whatever the facts, people's conceptions about the social role of schooling have changed markedly in recent centuries.

Because most societies do not behave as if they had a compelling interest in promoting education, as distinct from schooling, there has been no attempt to measure the effects of schooling on the growth of education. There has therefore been a natural tendency to confuse the two, despite the evident difference in their aims. This confusion often leads people who have been schooled, and their teachers, to believe that they are thereby educated. By failing to recognize that education is a lifetime task, they devalue its spiritual currency, and help to cast it into a disrepute that belongs more appropriately to those who are unable to distinguish the two.

THE FUNCTIONS OF SCHOOLING

Despite debate over education and its relation to schooling, few would deny that American schools do perform important functions. These can be classified as *socialization,* a unifying and disciplinary force in a society of diverse origins; *sorting,* an aspect of socialization that identifies people's future socioeconomic roles; *custody,* the child-sitting function; *knowledge and skills training,* developing a literate population, with at least a minimum of job-related skills; and encouragement of such attributes as *creativity and self-reliance,* which, according to many critics, is least well performed by the schools.

These functions have diverse relationships to education. Depending on how they are conducted, they can contribute to educational development or conflict with it. The effectiveness of schooling can, in large part, be considered apart from the quality of education. Many authors, notably educational reformers, argue that the schools *do* have an important effect on education, through the socializing function. Some, for example, contend that the schools, in sorting out talent for future career roles, instill in students an acceptance of the competitive and hierarchical social order and their role in it. Good students are, in the value system of the schools, considered more meritorious than poor students and therefore better fit for higher education and for prestigious jobs.

The acceptance of the existing social order so inculcated is an important element of people's education. But it is not clear how much of this inculcation reflects the effects of schooling. It seems at least equally likely that the values of schools and those of children both reflect the values of the existing social order, and no causal relationship is involved. If this is true, the schools' role as a socializing agency is primarily to transmit the larger society's values, rather than to exert an independent effect.

If some such view of the relationship between education and schooling is accepted, the question "How effective is schooling?" becomes the most appropriate one to ask of the school system. This formulation avoids the question of education, because education comes primarily from the family, from society as a whole, and from individual action and introspection. It would be unfair to praise or blame the schools for the degree to which the United States is a nation of educated people, because that is not what society asks the schools to produce.

We may well ask whether the schools should or could lay greater stress on encouraging their clientele to educate itself—since education is largely a do-it-yourself process, once the enabling conditions are met. It may be that over the next few generations, the primacy of economic considerations in schooling could decline, and American school systems could reshape their priorities. But for the present, any such aim seems visionary for the great majority of schools. As long as the schools continue to be dominated by the perceived needs of industrial society, the growth of educated men and civilized societies will remain largely outside the domain of schooling.

HOW WELL DO SCHOOLS PERFORM?

In evaluating the performance of today's school systems, we should probably confine ourselves to assessing those functions that schools do try to perform: socialization, sorting, custody, knowledge and skills training, and encouragement of certain individual attributes.

The *socialization* and *sorting* functions are often viewed as supporting the political and social status quo. Because there is a close association between years of schooling and socioeconomic status, and between test scores and years of schooling, the current system allegedly perpetuates the existing order of society. Critics of that order state that schooling lends it the cloak of legitimacy by treating years of schooling and test score results as objective determinants of merit. In fact, according to the critics, test scores and years of schooling are largely determined by heredity and environment, so that merit as defined by the student's own effort has little to do with the outcomes. The schools, like other social institutions, indoctrinate students to accept the legitimacy of the existing system, and its discipline, providing only the illusion of equality without providing equal opportunity.

The *custodial* function is also under widespread attack. Many observers have described the schools as operating in a joyless and mindless atmosphere, where the chief aim is to maintain a disciplinary and instructional lockstep. The custodial function is often overlooked in discussions of the school system. Yet, with the progressive elimination of minors from the labor force, the custodial function is increasingly important as a way of supervising the activities of youth.

In the traditional ideology of the schools, provision of *knowledge and skills* is the main element of schooling. The fact that children learn reading, mathematics, and foreign languages is strong evidence that schools do indeed play that role. But many studies, both statistical and observational, indicate little, if any, difference in the effectiveness of different schools in providing these skills. As noted above, most of the differences in measured learning reflect the influence of heredity and the nonschool environment. It seems likely that on the average the United States is on a par with other rich nations in the levels of knowledge and skills of the public at large, but in this respect American schools seem to fail the poor and minority groups.

The fifth function, *development of important personal attributes,* such as creativity and self-reliance, has also been called into question. Many critics claim that the schools are more likely to stifle such attributes than to promote them. Others claim that the schools are not an important factor in the development of these qualities. Finally, many of those who conduct research in child development agree that such qualities can be affected by schooling, but are at a loss to devise acceptable measures of *how* schools affect such attitudes or behavior.

SCHOOLING AND SOCIAL NORMS

In short, the effectiveness of schooling is under attack, with respect to each of its main functions. Some of the criticisms apply to the nature of American society, rather than to the schools themselves. It seems inappropriate to blame public schools for training people to conform to social norms. Presumably, public schools everywhere must always be strongly influenced by current norms. Therefore, the issues bifurcate into how well the schools carry out socially approved functions and how well they carry out reformers' designs.

Under existing norms, it is likely that the schools do reasonably well. Public opinion polls indicate that most people believe their local schools are doing a good job. On the other hand, most people also feel that schools should be doing more for poor people and minorities to provide "equal educational opportunity" for those who start out with a disadvantage. The evidence of statistical analyses and observation is strong: By current social standards the public schools are not doing well by these children along any of the five dimensions of schooling. It might be argued that these children are being properly socialized for the low status they can anticipate. However, the widespread sentiments of defeat and hostility that schooling seems to engender among the disadvantaged and the de facto inequality of opportunity they observe calls any such conclusions into serious question.

There is little empirical evidence that simply putting more resources into the schooling of the disadvantaged will in fact result in improvement of knowledge, as customarily measured. On this basis, many observers have denied the value of spending more money on disadvantaged children's schooling. However, they are only considering one outcome of compensatory education. It seems likely that better custody would result from higher spending, and it is at least possible that socialization and sorting functions might be better fulfilled as a consequence.

It is also possible that new and untested approaches to schooling will bring significant returns in reading achievement from higher spending. But at the present stage of experimentation, the evidence is lacking and is likely to emerge slowly, if at all, partly because organized school systems resist radical change and because achievement "gains" are hard to measure.

The demand for compensatory education is related to the issue of racial integration in the schools. Many of the disadvantaged children are black or Spanish-speaking, attending racially or ethnically isolated schools. Under judicial pressure, many southern cities and some northern ones have been forced to mix races in the public schools, by busing children within school districts. The legal argument is that segregated schools are inherently unequal, and therefore unconstitutional. The "educational" argument, whose validity remains unconfirmed, is that lower-class black and Spanish-speaking children will do better schoolwork if they are together with middle-class children who, in the event, are mostly white and English-speaking.

Social norms about racial integration in the schools are ambivalent. Most Americans have no objection to their children attending integrated schools, if the percentages of ethnic minorities are not high. But most white parents and many black parents object to compulsory busing as a means of integration. In other words, the public generally approves of the aim of school integration, but disapproves of the most generally feasible means.

This ambivalence is partly resolved in middle-class perspective by support for compensatory education as a socially accepted substitute for the presumed advantages of busing. The evidence on these advantages is unclear, and still in dispute. To the extent that they do exist, they are probably more educational (helping people learn to live and work with a variety of races and classes) than scholastic (improving minorities' academic performance). But the modest pace of school integration since 1954 indicates both that other social norms compete successfully with educational improvement, and that school systems are unwilling or unable to reject those competing norms. From this perspective, the present uncertain state of the school integration movement mirrors the public's own uncertainties, and in some sense therefore the schools are adhering relatively well to a complex and confusing set of signals from society.

REFORM OR REVOLUTION?

From some reformers' viewpoint the failings of the system are widespread, affecting all clients of the schools, and extending to all the major functions of schooling, as discussed above. Although reformers' proposed remedies vary, a survey of the reform literature points to a number of common themes that tend to conflict with current social values, as defined operationally by what people and institutions *do,* instead of what they say. In general, when they address the topic, school reformers favor racial integration in the schools. But their main targets are related—conformity, mindlessness in curriculum and discipline, destruction of creativity. They believe that society exacts too high a price for purchasing the conformity of youth to existing social values.

The remedies they propose are radical by contemporary standards. They want far less formal structure in the school and classroom. At one extreme, reformers propose that compulsory schooling be abolished in favor of voluntary association for teaching and learning, while others press for more modest changes modeled on the experience of some British primary schools.

Although they agree generally on the defects of the existing system and on the focus that remedies should take, the reform writers fail to state *how* society can be induced to adopt their proposals. Their failure is not trivial. As they themselves point out, the present school system operates as it does because, except for disadvantaged students, it generally meets social demands and is—partly for that reason—more acceptable to the school bureaucracy than the proposed reforms.

Broadly speaking, these reformers are seeking to transform schooling into an educational enterprise. Stated this way, the dimensions of their aims loom large, and it should be no surprise that society has so far ignored or misconstrued them, as it did the recommendations of John Dewey earlier in the century. It is difficult enough to install reforms that improve the functioning of the system, given its aims—racial desegregation in public schools is a case in point. It is far more difficult to install reforms that ask the schools to modify their social role; yet this is ultimately what the reformers, even the moderate ones, are asking. The informal classroom is not simply a reform of pedagogic method; it is a new relationship between student and teacher, and, necessarily, between student and society—and one that neither schools nor society appears ready to accept.

Most of the important social institutions face a similar tension between the conceptions that reformers seek to apply, and the accommodations that society requires in order to function. Reformers pursue ambitious and austere visions of an educated society, a just society, a religious society, while the social system requires only that the public be schooled, law-abiding, and churchly.

Changes in schooling aimed at providing education are correctly perceived not as reforms but as social revolutions, unprecedented in breadth because they would be based on the premise of equal educational opportunity rather than equal opportunities for schooling or enrichment. Thus, society would for the first time be offering everyone opportunities for independent self-development, rather than confining those opportunities to the few. Right now, no one in or out of the schools knows how to do this for even a few thousand students at a time, let alone fifty million.

It is surely no exaggeration to say that the consequent changes in society would dwarf those produced by the political and economic revolutions in eighteenth-century France and twentieth-century Russia and China. We have no conception of what a truly open society would be like, because society has always been elitist with respect to opportunities for education. Conservative philosophers such as Ortega y Gasset have argued, with some cogency, that mass culture is if anything the enemy of civilization and that mass civilization is unthinkable. If it is in fact thinkable (although possibly inconsistent with important psychological drives), this is the ultimate implication of the innocuous-sounding "informal classroom," and no one can see across the gulf that separates us from its attainment.

THE DIRECTIONS OF REFORM

Since it is axiomatic that society will not deliberately subsidize its own transformation, it seems realistic to ask what reforms in schooling are both desirable and possible in the present context. The most likely include

- ☐ Using new technologies to allow each student to study independently, at his own optimum pace and style, and to allow adults to continue their schooling away from the campus.
- ☐ Offering adults "mid-career" opportunities to develop new skills or improve on existing ones.
- ☐ Continuing experimentation with new approaches to schooling—experimental schools, educational vouchers, integrating schooling with workplaces.
- ☐ Experimenting further with educational accountability—initiatives with merit pay, the spread of public information on outcomes of schooling.
- ☐ Developing large-scale government programs for day care and early education, particularly for children of the poor.

The educational and pedagogical effects of these reforms are uncertain. But of more importance for the disadvantaged than any of these reforms will be a gradual improvement in their relative school performance, reflecting the steady rise of average years of schooling for the poor and minority groups.

Today, the average black male goes to school about as long as the average white male. Within a generation, this accomplishment will be reflected in the academic performance of his children. Aspirations for instant equality in academic performance are off the mark. But for reasons discussed above, the continued pressure for compensatory education promises substantial improvement in other dimensions of schooling.

The more ambitious aims of the educational reformers, seeking to build a base for civilization by transforming the schools and their values, will long be confined to a small number of experimental and private schools. The greening of American education that they seek, with its concomitant social reconstruction, is destined to remain for a long time on the agenda of aspirations, exerting a modest civilizing influence on a society whose eyes are fixed on other goals.

ABOUT THE AUTHOR: Economist John Pincus (Ph.D., Harvard) directs Rand's Education and Human Resources Program. He began his professional career on the State Department management staff and as a Point Four program officer on the India desk. Since joining Rand in 1961, he continued to serve State as consultant to the Department's Policy Planning Council. He has also advised the Office of European Economic Cooperation, the United Nations Conference on Trade and Development, and the International Bank for Reconstruction and Development. At Rand Dr. Pincus' main interests now focus on problems of education and of state and local government. Among his forthcoming publications are How Effective Is Schooling? *(Educational Technology Press) and* School Finance in Transition, *both to be published in 1974.*

... no inhuman power condemns us to live perpetually in the grim jail of our own ideas.

Fred Charles Iklé

Can Nuclear Deterrence Last Out the Century?

Extracts from a paper written for the California Arms Control and Foreign Policy Seminar and also published, in a shorter version, in Foreign Affairs, *January 1973. The Seminar was established by The Ford Foundation and is jointly sponsored by the California Institute of Technology and by Rand.*

The autumn of last year marked half the road from the beginning of the nuclear era to the year 2000. Mankind has been spared nuclear devastation since the annihilation of two Japanese cities by the only two nuclear weapons then existing.

But the destructiveness of nuclear arsenals, now increased many thousandfold, has sunk into human consciousness like man's knowledge of his mortality.

We all turn away, however, from the thought that nuclear war may be as inescapable as death, and may end our lives and our society within this generation or the next. We plan and work every day for the twenty-first century—as parents educating our children, as young workers saving for retirement, as a nation that seeks to preserve its physical environment, its political traditions, its cultural heritage. For this larger horizon—encompassing for the younger generation simply the common expectation of a healthy life—we do in fact assume "nuclear immortality." We believe, or we act as if we believe, that thanks to a certain international order, the existing arsenals of nuclear weapons with their almost incomprehensible destructiveness will never be used.

Yet, this order is so constructed that it cannot move toward abolition of nuclear weapons. It demands, as the necessary condition for avoiding nuclear war, the very preservation of these arms, always ready to destroy entire nations.

This ever-present danger once caused great anguish among the informed public in Western countries and evoked a diffused anxiety everywhere. Since the mid-1960s, the concern of both the public and the specialists has become far less acute, even though Soviet strategic forces have grown dramatically. Since 1968, confidence has been encouraged by the prospect of agreement in the Strategic Arms Limitation Talks (SALT) and, in May 1972, by the Moscow accords.

These initial agreements are designed, at least from the American perspective, first to preserve mutual deterrence as the strategic relationship between the United States and the Soviet Union, and second, to stabilize it by curbing the buildup of nuclear forces. As seen by a majority of American government officials, congressional leaders, and civilian experts, these two objectives should govern our strategic arms control policy as well as our own force planning for the foreseeable future. Other objectives (such as protecting cities) are held to jeopardize deterrence, and massive arms reductions or general and complete disarmament are considered utopian as well as dangerous.

According to this view, there are no alternatives to our current approach to mutual deterrence that deserve serious consideration. Even though the military services, government agencies, and experts may differ on particular points of doctrine and choices of weapons, the dominant view of the workings of mutual deterrence has come to uphold three far-reaching dogmas:

One: Our nuclear forces must be designed almost exclusively for "retaliation" in response to a Soviet nuclear attack— particularly an attempt to disarm us through a sudden strike.

Two: Our forces must be designed and operated in such a way that this "retaliation" can be swift, inflicted through a single, massive, and—above all—prompt strike. What would happen after this strike is of little concern for strategic planning.

Three: The threatened "retaliation" must be the killing of a major fraction of the Soviet population; moreover, the same ability to kill our population must be guaranteed the Soviet government in order to eliminate its main incentive for increasing Soviet forces. Thus, deterrence is "stabilized" by keeping it mutual.

This third dogma dictates not only our desire that Russian cities should remain essentially undefended, but also our willingness to abstain from defending our cities and even to hobble our capability to destroy Soviet nuclear arms. Proponents of this arrangement argue that it will lead to "arms race stability"; critics maintain that guaranteeing capabilities for Mutual Assured Destruction is indeed a "MAD" strategy.

Soviet military writers, by and large, express other views. Above all, they reject the idea that their forces should be designed for retaliation only, stressing instead the need to be prepared for fighting a nuclear war. Among Americans interested in nuclear strategy, however, only a minority now oppose any of these dogmas, and fewer still would reject them all. Absence of any one of these three elements—it is widely believed—would undermine deterrence, stimulate an arms race, or both.

Yet, these assumed requirements of stable deterrence are to a large extent the heritage of strategic policies from prior decades, now obsolete. They are a perilous way to protect ourselves from nuclear catastrophe and harmful to the prospects of strategic disarmament. Happily, they are dispensable for deterrence. Over the decades to come, we can develop and put into effect a safer and more humane strategy to prevent nuclear war.

DETERRENCE OF "RATIONAL" WAR

It was Winston Churchill who in 1955 first expounded the essential ideas of mutual deterrence to the world at large. In that celebrated "balance of terror" speech, he made a "formidable admission," as he himself called it: "The deterrent does not cover the case of lunatics or dictators in the mood of Hitler when he found himself in his final dugout. This is a blank." The most disturbing defect, today, in the prevalent thinking on nuclear strategy is the cavalier disregard for this blank. . . .

[EDITOR'S NOTE: Iklé argues that successful deterrence does not ensure the prevention of nuclear war, that our strategy does not deal with the possible acts of irrational leaders or with war that might start from a nuclear accident. Moreover, our concentration on deterring an enemy's "rational" decision assumes that a particular and narrow type of rationality governs our opponents' thinking.]

What a sad irony that the nations that had to fight Hitler to his last bunker should now rely on an interlock of their military postures, making survival depend on the rationality of all future leaders in all major nuclear powers.

RISK OF ACCIDENTAL WAR

In the 1950s, prior to the missile age and Russia's massive buildup of her nuclear forces, one heard a great deal about the

risk of accidental war. Now, when American and Soviet
missiles by the thousands are poised in constant readiness, this
concern has curiously diminished. To justify this more relaxed
attitude, some might point to the fact that no unauthorized
detonation has ever occurred, or cite the American-Soviet
agreements of 1971 for improving the hotline, or recall the
elaborate safeguards with which the military seem to protect
nuclear weapons. . . .

[EDITOR'S NOTE: Iklé points out, however, that nuclear
safeguards do not rule out the possibility of accidents, and
"our societies cannot survive by learning through trial and
error." The peril may be greater on the Soviet side, less open
to scrutiny. "Various influential people have urged that the
United States adopt procedures to launch its missile force
upon receipt of a warning that a Soviet surprise attack is on
the way," a point of view supported by Soviet strategic
thinking and by military institutional pressures.]

President Nixon, in his last two foreign policy messages, has
rejected a launch-on-warning policy. However, should one side
give the appearance of adopting it, the other might feel
compelled to institute faster launch procedures, creating an
"arms race" in reducing safeguards against accidental war.

The very fact that well-informed and well-intentioned advisers
now recommend, in essence, that the balance of terror should
rest on hair-triggered doomsday machines offers a chilling
reminder that we cannot rely on unswerving rationality
among those who might affect critical strategic decisions.

The launch-on-warning aberration is only the most
conspicuous outgrowth of the belief that to prevent nuclear
war we have but to deter it. Our present strategic policy
aggravates the risk of accidental war through many less
visible practices as well as by its grand design.

RETALIATION: A SWIFT, MASSIVE STRIKE?

While the current overemphasis on mutual deterrence against
a "rational" surprise attack dates from the mid-1960s, the
other two dogmas of our nuclear strategy are largely the

legacy of earlier periods. This is particularly true of the dogma that "retaliation" must be swift, inflicted in an all-out strike. . . .

[EDITOR'S NOTE: Iklé sees the origin of this dogma in the years when a Soviet invasion of Western Europe was seen as an imminent threat. The U.S. strategic force was then designed to fight such a war by quickly disarming the Soviet Union of its nuclear capability.]

[This emphasis on a quick disarming strike is in contradiction to our global deterrence posture of] "mutual assured destruction" [that] now has to meet the opposite requirement: to eschew, and through agreement mutually to preclude, a nuclear disarming capability. . . . [Starting about 1960] Soviet intercontinental missiles began to pose the canonical threat that figures so prominently in our strategic analysis—the massive surprise attack to disarm the United States. Given that the major portion of our strategic forces had been designed primarily for the prompt disarming strike in response to a Soviet invasion of Europe, they had not been primarily designed to survive a Soviet nuclear attack. For this new mission—"retaliation" in response to the Soviet nuclear strike—our bombers and missiles had to be launched promptly, before they were all destroyed on the ground. Here was [another] reason conspiring to keep our strategic thinking riveted to the notion that "retaliation" had to be swift.

"ASSURED MUTUAL GENOCIDE"

Clearly distinguishable from the notion that "retaliation" must be a swift, massive strike in any strategy of mutual deterrence is the now equally prevalent dogma that this strike must be designed to kill millions of people. This dogma can also be traced to the technical and conceptual limitations of strategic bombing in World War II. One has to recall the emotions and theories behind Hitler's raids on Coventry and London, and the deliberate bombing of residential areas in Hamburg, Tokyo, Dresden, and Hiroshima, to understand how we could have arrived where we are today. After World War II, military experts began to recognize that the immensely greater destructive power of nuclear weapons could compensate for the inaccuracy of aerial bombing, hence permitting destruction of small-size military targets. . . . [But a] nuclear weapon small enough to avoid vast civilian damage, yet accurate enough to hit most military targets, was not within the technology of the first nuclear decade.

As our strategic planners began to grapple with the role of nuclear weapons, not only was their vision confined by these technological limitations, but their sensitivity to the distinction between combatants and civilians—long cultivated through civilizing centuries—had become dulled by the strategic bombing in World War II. . . .

This history—not reasoned strategic analysis—led us into the habit of thinking that one had to threaten the killing of millions and millions of people in order to deter an "aggressor". . . .

Our arms control experts and military planners insulate themselves from the potential implications of their labors by layers of dehumanizing abstractions and bland metaphors. Thus, "assured destruction" fails to indicate what is to be destroyed; but then "assured genocide" would reveal the truth too starkly. The common phrase, "deterring a potential aggressor," conveys a false simplicity about the processes that might lead to a nuclear attack, as if we had to worry only about some ambitious despot who sits calculating whether or not to start a nuclear war. A moral perversity lies hidden behind the standard formula: In the event this "aggressor" attacks, we must "retaliate by knocking out *his* cities." Tomás de Torquemada, who burned 10,000 heretics at the stake, could claim principles more humane than our nuclear strategy, for his tribunals found all his victims guilty of having knowingly committed mortal sin.

The jargon of American strategic analysis works like a narcotic. It dulls our sense of moral outrage about the tragic confrontation of nuclear arsenals, primed and constantly perfected to unleash widespread genocide. It fosters the current smug complacence regarding the soundness and stability of mutual deterrence. It blinds us to the fact that our method for preventing nuclear war rests on a form of warfare universally condemned since the Dark Ages—the mass killing of hostages. . . .

In the long run, preserving a mutual threat of genocide may impede the reduction of tension and distrust between the two nuclear superpowers that we all hope for. It is far better, of course, for major powers to maintain peace between them by planning for deterrence instead of for war. But to stabilize deterrence by keeping ready arsenals for instant and unrestrained slaughter of men, women, and children is likely to impose a wrenching perspective on the officialdom of both nations. . . .

Despite the arcane jargon of modern deterrence theory, ordinary Americans and Russians cannot escape the realization that their generation and their children's generation are destined to remain the chosen target of the nuclear forces on the other side. Toward each other as a people, Americans and Russians harbor practically no feelings of hostility, but by our theories they must indefinitely face each other as the most fearful threat to their future existence.

BUILDING A SAFER FUTURE

Mercifully, no inhuman power condemns us to live perpetually in the grim jail of our own ideas. Alternatives can be found, although it may take decades to construct a better order for the prevention of nuclear war, and the task will require the work of many minds. This is all the more reason for beginning today.

A good place to begin is to cast out the dogma that to deter nuclear attacks, the threatened response must be the mass killing of people. By taking advantage of modern technology, we should be able to escape the evil dilemma that the strategic forces on both sides must either be designed to kill people or else jeopardize the opponent's confidence in his deterrent. The potential accuracy of "smart" bombs and missiles and current choices in weapon effects could enable both sides to avoid the killing of vast millions and yet to inflict assured destruction on military, industrial, and transportation assets—the sinews and muscles of the regime initiating war. Combined with this change in concept and techniques of "retaliation," we must design solutions more stable than in the past to the problem of achieving invulnerable deterrent forces. No matter how accurately each side can aim its own weapons, we want to make it physically impossible for most of the strategic arms to be destroyed by sudden attack.

It is premature to judge whether such a change in capabilities and doctrine might eventually make it desirable for us and the Russians to permit active defenses for urban populations while prohibiting them for military assets other than the nuclear deterrent. If such discrimination were to become technically feasible, its desirability would depend not only on American-Soviet relations at that time, but also on the danger of attack, if any, from other nuclear powers.

The second dogma we have to discard is that response to nuclear attack must be the prompt, even instant, launching of nearly the entire nuclear force. By eliminating the need to design our arms for instant launching, we can reduce vulnerability in many new ways. Precisely how to design forces that are far less vulnerable because they are not meant for instant reaction is a task for future research. . . .

If we can eliminate the vulnerability of our strategic arms to surprise attack, we will have broken the vicious circle: that they must be ready for prompt launching because they are vulnerable, and that they are vulnerable because they must be ready. Furthermore, should the Russians come to agree with us, we could jointly decide to replace the doomsday catapults invented in the 1950s with arms that are incapable of being launched swiftly. If the strategic order could be transformed in this way, the dominant fear of surprise attack which drives our arms competition would loosen its grip. Weapons incapable of quick launching tend to be less suitable for surprise; and against truly invulnerable nuclear armaments, surprise would have lost its purpose.

Neither we nor the Russians will suddenly scuttle all our hair-triggered engines of destruction. By abandoning the dogma of speed, however, both of us can shift intellectual energies and budgetary resources to develop different nuclear armaments. Strategic weapons have a long lifetime; between the initial concept and the scrap heap, up to 25 years may elapse. What we engineer during this decade will have to prevent nuclear war into the next century.

Discarding the dogma of speed would result in another gain, perhaps even more important than reduced vulnerability. It would go a long way to reduce the danger of accidental war. By eliminating the requirement for launching entire missile forces in a matter of minutes, we can get rid of the triggering mechanisms and sensitive command procedures where some obscure malfunction might lead to cataclysm. Time is the best healer of mistakes, whether technical or human. . . .

Deterrence would remain: The conventional military might of the aggressor nation—its navy, army, and air force with their logistics support—would be the first to suffer "assured destruction." Such a prospect would make even less tempting the planning of nuclear war than today's actual or imagined opportunities for a quick strike to deprive the opponent of his nuclear weapons. And the risk of the destruction of cities would still loom in the background.

Could the Soviet leaders be induced to accept such an evolution? We have lately devoted a major effort to teach our dogmas to the Russians—some feel with considerable success. Certain stubborn positions in Soviet strategic thought, however, manifest a less narrow view of deterrence by showing greater concern for dangers of a nuclear war that cannot be deterred, and reflect a longer time-perspective than we have developed. Once freed from our dogmas, we may discover that the distance in strategic views between us and the Russians is less than it appears today.

The greatest obstacles to the necessary reconstruction of our strategic order may well be intellectual and institutional rigidities. We justify our old habits of thinking because we are so competently familiar with the arguments against change. We are disposed to reject suggestions for improvement by demanding a perfect solution at the outset. . . .

The scholasticism justifying our current policy is full of contradictions. On the one hand, we brush aside the immorality of threatening to kill millions of hostages, assuming that the threat will deter and that to deter means to prevent nuclear war. On the other hand, we argue that we must be poised to carry out "retaliation" swiftly and thus convey determination for irrational vengeance, since all rational purpose of retaliation would have disappeared when its time had come. We want to maintain a vague threat of using nuclear weapons first to deter massive conventional attack; yet, to stabilize mutual deterrence we must not threaten Soviet nuclear arms nor defend against them. . . .

The result of such contradictions is a cancelling out of good intentions. In some years, our arms policy is dominated by our preoccupation with the arms race and the view that we should therefore hobble our forces. In other years, we decide to refurbish our so-called options for attacking Russia's nuclear arms. Left to itself, this pulling and hauling between *yin* and *yang* will not lead the world into a safer era. On the contrary, the bureaucratic struggle may result in the worst compromise among the biases of contending factions. While luck has been with us so far, strategic thinking must and can find a new path into the twenty-first century.

ABOUT THE AUTHOR: Fred Iklé has written widely on arms control issues, international negotiations, and other political and social issues. He is the author of The Social Impact of Bomb Destruction, How Nations Negotiate, *and* Every War Must End. *He joined the Rand staff in 1955 and left in 1961 to go to the Harvard Center for International Affairs. In 1964 he became Professor of Political Science at the Massachusetts Institute of Technology. He returned in 1968 to head Rand's Social Science Department. Dr. Iklé left Rand in 1973 to become Director of the U.S. Arms Control and Disarmament Agency.*

We will all of us continue, like the drunk, to hunt for our lost wallet under the lamppost, not because we're sure it's there, but because the light is good.

Peter L. Szanton

Systems Problems in the City

Several years ago, in a large American city, a group of analysts—engineers, mathematicians, economists, and others—set out to assist the city government. They launched thirty or forty separate studies. Let me describe two of them.

A POLICE STORY

One had to do with the police. The study found that two-thirds of the force was on duty during the hours when only half the crime occurred, the remaining one-third of the force having to respond to the other half, which occurred during the evening hours. This imbalance appeared to be required by an old law. The analysts proposed a procedure for observing the law, and still almost doubling the number of men on duty during the high-crime hours. But the policemen's union, which was militant and powerful, opposed such a change.

So the administration decided to try to repeal the old law. As it happened, the leading newspaper of the city just then began publishing a series of articles detailing how police actually spent their time. One article was accompanied by a photograph showing several patrol cars parked together, with all occupants fast asleep. The new law passed.

That was in the spring, and the mayor was up for reelection in the fall. Crime in the streets was one of the principal issues, so the mayor promised speedy implementation of the new law. But the police department moved slowly. There were no patrol cars available for many of the men to be redeployed. The police commissioner argued, moreover, that several thousand additional patrolmen would have to be hired. This seemed unnecessary to the mayor's aides, but they were now in midcampaign and preoccupied. The analysts might have addressed the question, but by then they were viewed by the police as agents of the mayor, by the mayor as useful only for providing theoretical solutions, and by themselves as skaters on thin ice, with the day warming rapidly.

There were no funds for additional men, or for new cars. So the innovation was attempted only partially—mainly in the form of foot patrolmen in selected areas of the city. Some of the areas selected had the clearest need for additional protection; some seemed to be those in which the mayor's political problems were most acute. The mayor was narrowly reelected that fall.

But what became of the new police deployment pattern, and what were the effects on crime? The appearance is that now, several years later, the reallocated men are neither effectively supervised, nor well equipped, nor optimally located. The effect on crime rates is favorable, but quite small.

Let me resist for a moment the temptation to generalize from these facts, and turn instead to the second study.

A HOUSING STORY

The second group of analysts was concerned about the housing problem in the city. There was general agreement among officials as to what that problem was: It took far too much time and money to produce new publicly assisted housing units. Construction targets were not being met, and clamor for additional housing was increasing rapidly. The analysts should find new methods for making construction faster and cheaper. Interestingly, the analysts slowly came to disagree. This is a summary of what one of them wrote:

"As our studies progressed, we became increasingly convinced that the traditional emphasis of city housing policy on new construction was unserviceable. We came to believe that the attention of city officials should be focused on saving the existing stock from the growing threat of deterioration and abandonment, and that solutions should be sought on a city-wide scale. The pervasive problem was that most owners of the controlled housing were not getting enough revenue to maintain their buildings properly and still earn a reasonable return on capital. [This city still maintained a system of rent control first adopted during World War II.] The issue that was least clear was the extent to which these revenue shortages were directly due to rent control, as distinguished from the poverty of tenants.

"We launched or provided technical assistance in a number of studies designed to prove and test these views. By early the following year, we were sure we had a case, and began to formulate a strategy. We recommended raising ceiling rents to cover standard full costs, much in the pattern of public utility rate-setting; a program of direct rent assistance to low-income families to offset the rent increases; improved code enforcement as a check on landlord delinquency; and a special program addressed to persistently substandard buildings.

"It was a long, hard selling job. Every critical comment by someone whose opinion carried weight in administration circles sent us back to the drawing board. Our proposals concerning rent control were eventually accepted, due to a combination of factors:

☐ Our arguments were forcefully presented in a steady flow of briefings and documents.
☐ Our principal liaison with the agency was heavily committed to the enterprise and worked with tremendous energy and skill to advance the cause within the agency.
☐ The visible symptoms of trouble in the housing market increased and intensified, so the issues raised by our work continued to command official attention.

"The existing rent control statute was due to expire at the end of March 1970, unless renewed by the city council. The city council, the press, and the public began to demand that the administration reveal its plan. A newspaper acquired a bundle of draft material that had been circulated within the housing agency, including portions of our work, from which it quoted selectively in a series of news stories. The city council demanded access to this mysterious document; one group of councilmen sued for its release.

"With the issue thus forced, in February the housing administrator sent the city council a report containing our diagnosis of the rental housing crisis, our prognosis, and our recommendations. Finally, in May, the mayor sent his proposal for rent control reform to the city council. We were pleased to have it described in the press as close to our ideas. The city council enacted the reforms in June."

And in the two and a half years since that assessment was written, the rent control law has been implemented, progress has been made in the handling of persistently substandard buildings, code enforcement has been tightened, and experiments in rent assistance for families unable to pay the full costs of well-maintained housing have been undertaken by the federal government.

Yet, three months after approving the rent control reform, the city council began an investigation of the mayor's use of consultants. Its report, generally quite critical, recommended utilizing the analytic resources of a local university rather than those of the housing analysts' organization.

SOME LESSONS

These two stories, I think, are representative of many. What do they tell us?

One point they suggest is the tendency of our society to look first for problems of efficiency, and the dangers of that tendency. We want more output for a given cost, or the same output at lower cost. And where new technology or new techniques promise those efficiency gains, the game looks all the more attractive. So we play it—in business, in government, in warfare. And too frequently—in government and in warfare—we lose. We lose not because efficiency gains are illusory, or unattainable, or unimportant, but for two other reasons. The first is that actually achieving gains requires levels of managerial skill and of persistence rarely present in governments. The second is that even when such gains can be squeezed out, they too often succeed only in strengthening policies that miss the point. The most useful act of the housing analysts, you recall, was their first—their refusal to accept the housing production problem as the right one, and their insistence instead on stemming the premature decay of existing housing. The problem was not to turn the faucet on harder; it was to plug the drain.

Governments are better at recognizing problems than at identifying their causes. And the larger or more complex the system in which the problem appears, the less likely is the first attribution of cause to be right. The analyst who wishes to be useful must be prepared, then, to insist on exploring for himself the conundrum of cause.

The second principle exemplified by the stories, it seems to me, is that even when the right problem (or one of the right problems) is being addressed, engineers, operations researchers, and economists want to address it solely in terms of their professional skills. They perform their calculations, identify an apparent solution, and present it to the client. At that point they believe their job is done. Their training tells them they have reached the limits of their professional competence. Their stomachs tell them the rest is politics, which is dangerous, or management, which is dull. They want no further responsibility, and may be offered none. In a sense, this too is a variant of the efficiency curse. The analyst wants to function simply as analyst; that is the only function in which he imagines he has a comparative advantage.

But the system that must receive recommendations, understand them, dampen fears about them, modify them, try them, and live with their consequences, good and ill, is weak and vulnerable. And it is weakest where the problem is not "Where should we be going?" but "How do we get there—or somewhere near there—from here?" Ends and means interact. And to the degree they are separable, means pose the harder challenge. For both reasons, those who propose ends, and who care about outcomes, must care about means.

The third principle I abstract from the stories is simply that urban problems, like social issues generally, are harder than the military and industrial issues most engineers and operations researchers are familiar with. They are harder both to understand and to affect.

I do not mean that, analytically, they are tougher than the fundamental issues of business responsibility or of national security policy—which remain unsolved; I do not believe they are. But they are harder than the problems of cost control, physical systems design, inventory policy, and requirements forecasting, with which the quantitative analytic professions are familiar.

Major issues in such problem areas as housing and welfare, and even police work, may lack the starting point of accepted objectives. The analyst lacks any authoritative statement of what is to be maximized or minimized, and under what constraints. And his efforts to obtain such a statement are likely to end in frustration.

Urban governments—unlike industrial clients—persist in avoiding close specification of objectives. They must. The purposes of some programs are cynical; the objectives of many more are multiple, and maintaining disparate sources of support for them requires ambiguity. Moreover, men who run for office know far more poignantly than do researchers the odds against getting change actually accomplished. They know, therefore, that large promises made with specificity are invitations to proof of failure two or three years later. Yet large promises must be made. Hence, vagueness. The housing analysis was a case in point. The city in which that work was done spent $800 million annually on housing, but the analysts searched in vain for any description of what that vast sum was intended to purchase.*

And even when the intellectual difficulties are manageable, the actual accomplishment of proposed innovation is typically harder than in the industrial or defense contexts: The client's influence on his environment is far more tightly constrained. Obviously, neither military nor industrial organizations operate autonomously. But a city government attempting even to change simple work procedures must frequently gain not only the agreement of a powerful union, but affirmative action by a state legislature. (And in the urban case, the union members are also stockholders—they vote.) A major policy initiative will typically require the generation of public support, the approval of a city council, funding from both state and federal agencies, and at least the passive concurrence of ethnic or neighborhood or occupational groups with the power to prevent its execution.

In short, then, quantitatively oriented analysts first addressing urban problems encounter a number of difficulties. They find major issues—of cause, purpose, effect—analytically formidable; and minor ones—of efficiency—tractable and attractive. They believe that analysts advise, and officials decide and enforce. They learn only slowly that both decisionmaking and implementation are processes, not acts, and that both require the analysts' protracted participation. And they are appalled, even so, at the ability of bureaucracies, and of the larger society, to resist changes that seem to them so self-evidently rational. We must recognize, then, that social problems are a challenge for which we are not well equipped, and that meeting them will require changes in the way analysts typically operate.

SOME NEEDED CHANGES

First, we need to assemble a far greater breadth of interacting skills. We will all of us continue, like the drunk, to hunt for our lost wallet under the lamppost, not because we're sure it's there, but because the light is good. The corrective is that others see by other light. Systems engineers, operations researchers, statisticians, and economists will have to work in groups that include sociologists, decision theorists, retired union leaders, students of bureaucratic behavior, lawyers, former state senators, and urban historians. Only in this way can we enrich the researchers' understanding of the circumstances they see as problems—by making clear to them, for example, how a policy or procedure, ineffective in terms of its stated goals, may nonetheless serve powerful and perhaps legitimate but unspoken purposes.

Second, we need new kinds of institutions. Existing organizations can obviously do much of value. R&D firms, commercial management consultants, university-based urban studies groups, client-funded think tanks, consulting engineering firms—all have a legitimate and useful role to play. But analysts and researchers must be placed in a novel kind of relationship with officials. The analysts must be independent enough to be critical of city policies, insulated enough from daily operational concerns to work persistently on underlying problems, but close enough in their working relations with city agencies to produce recommendations that are timely, realistic, and usable. This combination of conditions is not well met within traditional organizational forms.

The necessary closeness and sense of involvement will depend on the incentives analysts have to measure their success—not in numbers of papers produced, or students trained, or new products sold, but in improvements actually accomplished in the government of cities. Providing these incentives and this measure of success will be one task of the new organizations. The intellectual independence of the analysts will derive partly from accepted standards of the analytic professions. But to survive over time, their independence must almost certainly be buttressed by funding from sources other than the client.

Cities should pay some substantial fraction of the cost. Some sacrifice of a city's resources to obtain the work helps ensure the necessary interest of officials in its progress and their attention to its outcome. But funding must not be tied too nicely to findings. And given the current budgetary situation of all major American cities, it is clear that no substantial program of policy research or analysis can long be funded by any of them. It must therefore be a second function of institutions seeking to work steadily and critically on major urban issues that they generate—and qualify for—additional sources of support. State governments may be induced to do something; foundations something more. But the bulk of such noncity funding must be derived, in one form or another, from the federal government.

Let me conclude by noting that a major advantage of the kind of intellectual and financial independence just imagined is that it may make more common a relationship currently almost unknown, but essential, I believe, to any substantial growth in effective governmental use of analytic work. It is the relationship between analysts and legislatures.

When they are drawn to governmental work at all, analytic organizations are drawn to work for the executive branch. Their common clients are the agencies, departments, and administrations of this branch. These are the entities that operate governmental programs, that increasingly are obliged to evaluate them, and that—if anyone does—have the funds to commission studies.

But information is a constituent of power. When analysts serve only one branch of a government, and the product of their work is accessible only to that branch, prior power relationships are altered. When analyses address problems of minor importance, the effect on relative power will be correspondingly small. But the more significant the analysis, the larger the effect, and the more likely the other branches—especially the legislature—will respond.

The response can take three forms: The legislature may seek to pry loose the withheld information; or to provide itself with corresponding analytic capacity; or to deny the executive the future use of such a resource. The first course will often be inappropriate and unsuccessful; executive agencies should have the power to assure to analysts and to themselves the confidentiality that makes candor possible. The second course is cumbersome, expensive, time-consuming, and unfamiliar to most legislatures. The third course is therefore likely to be the reflexive one: deny the executive the use of such consultants. Recall the position of the city council faced with the housing study.

But the virtue of having analytic competence in the service of legislatures—the second course—is not merely that it will blunt attacks on other analysts; it should also improve the quality and utility of analyses performed for both branches. The spur of competition, the anticipation of competent and critical review, the expanded availability of data—all should work toward a quality of policy analysis rarely achieved today.

---

* The analysts' response to the problem was ingenious. Their published report described three alternative objectives for the city's housing policy, and then—given the unwillingness of the political process explicitly to choose any one of them—explicitly chose one itself. Despite all the uproar that report precipitated, no one took issue with the choice of objectives. Indeed, no one appeared to notice that it had been the analysts who had made the choice. But inventing governmental objectives is an uncomfortable function for researchers, and properly so. It is likely to remain a rare and last resort.

ABOUT THE AUTHOR: Trained in history and the law (L.L.B., Harvard), Peter Szanton practiced law in New York City before joining the Department of Defense in 1962 as a planner concerned with European security matters. He subsequently moved to the Budget Bureau, where he became Deputy Director of its Program Evaluation Staff. In 1967 he joined Rand's Washington Office—and was quickly borrowed by the White House to serve on the President's Task Force on

Government Organization. He next headed the effort that led to the creation of The New York City–Rand Institute and served as its president until 1971, when he became a Fellow at Harvard's J. F. Kennedy School of Government. The following year he rejoined Rand at its Washington Domestic Research Center.

In a managerial sense, the elimination of the draft was a major shock.

Richard V. L. Cooper and
Bernard Rostker

Military Manpower in a Changing Environment

At no other time in our history has a peacetime military had to cope with so many changes in the way it deals with its most important resource, people. For a variety of reasons military manpower issues are a central concern in the Pentagon and on

Capitol Hill. Clearly, the military of the 1990s will be very different from the military of today. The process of change, which started in the 1960s, is apt to accelerate over the next several decades as new policies and procedures are instituted.

Already there have been fundamental changes within the military, in the relationship of the military and the general population, and within the whole of society. Paramount among these changes are the elimination of the draft, the changing foreign policy and resulting military strategy, the reduction in defense personnel and budgets, the increasing costs of personnel and personnel related services, and the personnel implications of an ever-increasing technological base. In addition, changing racial attitudes, a declining civilian manpower pool, and new attitudes toward the military in Congress and among the general population in the wake of the Vietnam war have created a new environment in which the military have to operate.

The American military have already begun to adapt to changes in the personnel environment; more change is likely. Although the overall strategies for change have not yet been developed and the precise form is not known, the need for change is recognized, and the direction it will take is evident. It is the purpose of this essay to examine some of the major manpower issues and possible alternatives to the present way people are managed and employed by the military.

THE DRAFT

Unlike many European countries, the United States has not developed an elitist military. The American military has generally operated as an integral part of American society, especially since the Second World War. The citizen soldier, whether on active service or in reserve, has been the principle upon which the military has developed. Today, most officers are trained through voluntary and part-time programs on university campuses, not by service academies. Enlisted personnel are procured from the general population, not from families with long histories of military service. Many have viewed the move to an all-volunteer armed force as one away from this historical pattern. Experience so far has not shown that a volunteer force will become mercenary and detached from American society. The challenge for the military, however, is to maintain a broad-based organization that can attract young people.

One of the major effects of the draft was to remove the military from the forces of the marketplace. In a draft environment, the military could afford to be dominated by traditions that often ran counter to the general thrust of changes in the civilian environment. The draft ensured an adequate supply of manpower, no matter what personnel policies the Services followed. The removal of the draft compels the military to compete in the civilian marketplace for qualified personnel. The Armed Forces must now be responsive to changes in the civilian environment to attract and retain sufficient numbers of qualified personnel at a cost the American public is willing to bear.

In setting personnel policies, the military do not necessarily have to emulate the civilian environment, for there may indeed be certain policies and traditions they will want to pursue that are not encountered in the civilian environment. Rather, they must develop policies that explicitly take into account the alternatives available in the civilian economy. For example, although the military pay and rank structure need not mirror that in the civilian economy, civilian opportunities must at least be accounted for in the design of military compensation and hierarchy. Further, not only must military personnel policies provide realistic alternatives to civilian employment, but the military should also recognize that there are valuable lessons to be learned from the civilian experience.

In a managerial sense, the elimination of the draft was a major shock. The draft had set up many internal behavioral and organizational responses that have had to be altered in the zero draft world. These patterns affect every aspect of the way the military manage and use their human resources. They have already made substantial progress in adjusting to the new environment, but the full effect of the ending of the draft and moves toward reducing personnel costs have not been felt.

The immediate effect of ending the draft was a substantial increase in the cost (both marginal and average) of new active-duty personnel. The Department of Defense estimates that the direct salary cost of transition to an all-volunteer force in fiscal year 1973 alone was 2.4 billion. In addition, 1.1 billion was spent in this year by the DOD to provide special pecuniary bonuses and such nonpecuniary benefits as new living quarters. Although the early indications are that a volunteer force is indeed a viable institution, the large costs associated with the procurement and retention of qualified personnel and the limited defense resources available suggest that alternatives for more efficient use of a limited number of high-quality personnel must be developed.

MANPOWER/PERSONNEL

The major responsibilities for procuring an all-volunteer force have been carried out by the personnel managers. However, by their very nature, personnel and supply considerations are reactive rather than proactive. The more substantive questions relating to cost are determined in the requirements process, which sets manpower standards and determines the military's demand for labor. In general, there has been a lack of response to increasing manpower costs as reflected in the pattern of labor usage over time. For example, one response to rising manpower costs is to substitute equipment for labor. Although labor has become over 50 percent more expensive than capital in the last fifteen years, there has been an insufficient response in terms of the share of military resources devoted to labor. The military ought to be looking for alternatives to become more capital intensive. For example, it may be appropriate to consider equipment with *throw-away* (i.e., replaceable) parts, rather than repairable parts. This is a form of substituting capital for labor, since less labor (in the form of less highly skilled personnel) can be used by maintaining a larger stock of parts inventories—i.e., more capital. The military may also wish to consider automation of supply lines as another form of substituting capital for labor. The use of resources—capital and labor—must become more responsive to the costs of those resources.

In fact, there are organizational and behavioral reasons for the lack of response to changes in the cost of manpower. In each of the Services and in the Office of the Secretary of

Defense, separate organizational entities determine the amount of labor required (manpower) and how those requirements are to be filled (personnel). As a result of the distinction, manpower costs seldom enter as a criterion for determining the structure of the military force. There are some notable exceptions—such as the recent cuts in the Minuteman crew force to reduce operating costs, and consideration of manpower costs in the Navy's ship acquisition process—but requirements are generally set without regard to personnel costs. Only when the individual requirements become aggregated into total Service budgets do planners begin to worry about costs. However, the lack of visibility at that level results in the types of gross adjustments that cut force structure rather than reallocate resources within the given force structure.

The reallocation of defense resources between capital and labor and among various types of labor has been further discouraged by the "manning doctrine" method of setting manpower requirements, both in the initial design of new weapons and operating systems and in the use of existing systems. As a result, alternative manning configurations are seldom explored. Only recently have manpower costs been given consideration in the design of new systems. Although attempts have been made to integrate logistics cost considerations in the design phase of new systems, little attention has been paid to how alternative systems configurations affect such manpower factors as training, procurement, and related personnel costs.

It has generally been argued that once a system is in the operating inventory, manning standards are relatively fixed. In fact, however, opportunities still remain for substituting one type of labor for another, thus affecting the operating costs of the system. For example, the F-4 aircraft was designed to be operated by two crew members. Originally the aircraft was manned by two pilots. The eventual substitution of a navigator for the second pilot substantially reduced the operating costs of the system. But in general, opportunities for substituting one type of labor resource for another are not examined in the manpower requirements process. Such considerations could result in substantial cost savings.

RESERVES

The removal of the draft has reduced the pressure for young men to join the reserves. As a result, the reserve forces are experiencing major shortfalls in their manpower procurement. The Army is currently more than 40,000 men short of its stated requirements. Further, recent research indicates that neither current pay nor proposed pay increases will be adequate to man the reserves at traditional levels.

If the Services are to have a volunteer reserve at pay scales similar to those now in use, they must develop alternative manning doctrines and become more efficient in the way they recruit. Current and forecast reserve shortfalls will force a rethinking of the reserve mission and the alternatives for accomplishing that mission. In particular, it may no longer be feasible to structure reserve units to look like active units. Effective management of reserve forces must take into account the increased costs of reserve personnel, and manning doctrines must be adjusted accordingly. At the same time, the Services must also investigate a variety of incentives aimed at increasing reserve enlistments (both nonprior service and prior service) and reenlistments. Controlled experimentation seems to be a useful tool in this regard. For example, the Army and the Air Force are beginning an experiment aimed at estimating the enlistment response to a shorter reserve commitment. Experimentation of this type permits inexpensive evaluation of alternative policies without committing the Services to options that may prove infeasible. Wider use of this research tool is imperative.

MILITARY OR CIVILIAN?

One of the central issues likely to develop as the pressure mounts to reduce personnel costs, and our overseas basing commitments decline, is the way civilian personnel are used by the Defense Department. The military have been under pressure to increase the use of civilian personnel since the mid-sixties. Discussion of the problems of substituting civilians for military personnel contains much anecdotal evidence but little supporting analysis. Many have argued that certain jobs should be considered to be truly military, not for combat reasons but because civilians are thought to be unwilling or too unresponsive to fill them. Others have countered that civilians can be hired if jobs are made available, since recruitment is said to be easier for civilians than for the military.

In general, arguments have centered on accomplishing short-run goals. Little consideration has been given to the tradeoff of cost and effectiveness or of cost and flexibility. There is often the implication that personnel situations that create problems for the military will not create similar problems if "civilianized." For example, retention is recognized as a military problem but is ignored in the case of civilians. Replacement of military positions with civilians will lower military accession and retention requirements, but it will have an unknown effect on the civilian personnel system. In fact, a consistent way of characterizing labor resources available to the Defense Department has not been developed. The real question is, how do the military and civilian forces differ in form and substance, and given the differences, what mix would enable the military to carry out their mission in the face of real and present operating constraints? At present, the tools needed to lift the discussion to a more general consideration of roles and use are not available.

COMPENSATION

Probably the largest area of military personnel policy subject to major revision is compensation and rank structure. Policies such as "up or out" must be reexamined in the light of civilian experience. The present system of promotion and reward places a premium on a calendar metric instead of proven human performance and capabilities. Further, those not wanting supervisory roles are *forced out,* even though they may be competent technicians.

The general system of compensation, promotion, and reward is out of date by some 25 years and is in drastic need of overhaul, since the types of personnel attracted and retained in the military may be *seriously and adversely* affected. An alternative might be a matrix structure of management similar to that developed by the West German Armed Forces.

The so-called matrix structure permits a more flexible system of management in which human performance and capabilities are the major determinants of pay and rank. In such a system, pay would be a function of both rank and job duties. An individual may remain in the work force or rise to a supervisory position, depending on his interests and capabilities.

Changing the compensation system would require a major philosophical shift in the way the military view pay. In general, all compensation schemes provide a reward for past service and an incentive for future action. Compensation systems that stress differential pay as a way of "meeting the market" are dominated by the latter, and those characterized by fixed pay tables and longevity stress the former. The U.S. military have traditionally viewed pay as a reward. All personnel of similar grade and years of service are paid comparable wages. Special pay is authorized in recognition of extra military-related services. However, hazardous-duty pay, flight pay, diving pay, and jump pay are all seen as rewards for performing special military functions and have become rights rather than a flexible management tool.

In recent years, and with much internal consternation, categories of incentive pay have been introduced. Proficiency pay, the variable reenlistment bonus, and the combat arms bonus are all examples of incentive pay. Furthermore, it is likely that in the future, extensions of incentive pay could provide considerable savings by allowing the military to meet both their internal and external market without raising the compensation of everyone in the force. In terms of internal markets, incentive compensation can be used to foster self-selection to remote stations or to perform less desirable duty. In terms of the external market, the Special Pay Act of 1973 is an example of a broad-based extension of incentive pay.

A further question is, why should the military provide tenure and guarantee retirement income to almost everyone in the force? Without vesting of pension rights, the military have been hesitant to discharge career personnel before they could qualify for their pensions at 20 years of service. One way individuals will more willingly self-select themselves out of the military is to provide vesting of pension rights. Such a system would provide for an equitable treatment of people who want to, or are forced to, leave the Services before a normal retirement. It should eliminate the "locked-in" effect that results in almost no turnover between the 10th and 20th year of service.

However, vesting would also mean that the military would have to be more competitive in attempts to keep their best people. In effect, vesting is a double-edged tool. It will create a better environment for early termination of less productive people before full retirement. However, it will also create the same incentives for the best people to leave.

Perhaps no other general compensation issue has received more attention than retirement. Yet the arguments surrounding the retirement issue seem to be missing the major factor driving both retirement costs and the military career structure—*the 20-year career.* Why should the military retire able-bodied young men and women in their late thirties or early forties when that time seems to be the most productive, as shown in the civilian environment?

The 30-year career has, in fact, been the historical norm. Between 1900 and 1935, all officers had to serve a minimum of 30 years before retirement. In 1935 the Army offered their officers voluntary early retirement at 15 years of service to minimize the effect of the World War I "hump." Enlisted personnel were required to serve 30 years until 1945, when the requirement was reduced to 20 years. By 1948 all Services had instituted 20-year retirements. Even today, Navy and Marine enlisted men technically serve a 30-year career, 10 of which can be spent in a reserve component.

Compensation and compensation policy must be viewed as a *tool* for efficient management of military human resources. Many practices that have evolved through tradition may have to be abandoned in the interest of a less costly force.

* * *

The need for change is clear and the importance of immediate action to resolve the problems described here must not be understated, for the policies that are adopted now will affect the military manpower system for some time to come.

ABOUT THE AUTHORS: Economists Richard Cooper and Bernard Rostker direct Rand's military manpower research for the Office of the Secretary of Defense (OSD) and for Air Force Project Rand.

Dr. Cooper, who took his Ph.D. (1971) under Arnold Zellner and Milton Friedman at the University of Chicago, joined Rand's Economics Department in 1971. Before assuming direction of Rand's OSD manpower research, he worked on problems associated with the management of the Air Force officer corps, the effects of removing procurement restrictions on foreign development assistance, and hospital costliness. He teaches econometrics and monetary theory part-time at the University of California at Los Angeles and at Santa Barbara, and at the Rand Graduate Institute for Policy Studies. He is also a consultant to the California Hospital Association.

Before joining Rand in 1970, Dr. Rostker (Ph.D., Syracuse) served two years as an economist in the Office of the Assistant Secretary of Defense (Systems Analysis). At Rand he has worked on Air Force logistics and manpower problems—primarily the status of air reserve personnel in a zero draft environment and, for the State of California, an incentive pay system for employment counselors who work with the disadvantaged. In 1972 Dr. Rostker taught the Manpower Seminar at the Rand Graduate Institute for Policy Studies. He is a senior staff member of the Economics Department.

Without a theory of climate, we cannot gauge the consequences of the interference of man with his environment....

W. Lawrence Gates

Understanding Climatic Change

There are few human activities that are not influenced in one way or another by climate. We know from the study of history that the growth and nature of early civilization, the patterns of migration, and the development of agriculture were all determined in large measure by the available rainfall and the severity of winter temperatures. Even today, the role of climate in such areas as food production, commerce and transportation, and the management of resources is clearly seen. And in a larger sense, climate plays an important role in many matters of national policy, and in international relations.

Man's attitude toward climate seems to have been dominated by either of two views. One, that the climate always has been the same (and therefore by extension always will be the same);

or two, that nothing could be done to alter the course of climatic changes in any case. The first view is certainly incorrect. We need only recall that as recently as 17,000 years ago much of North America was under a vast ice sheet, and that the Sahara Desert was once the site of tropical vegetation. Evidence of such widespread climatic variations in the distant past comes from a variety of indirect or proxy sources, such as sediments on the ocean bottom, tree-rings, glacier ice, and fossil pollen. Although their causes are not known, the earth has experienced many major climatic fluctuations in the past and probably will continue to do so in the future.

That the second view is incorrect is somewhat less certain. But the mere possibility that man *might* be able to change the climate in some way is of great importance. Without knowing the causes of climatic change, we cannot say a priori there are no ways in which we could possibly alter it. There is evidence, for example, that the earth's climatic regime is in rather delicate balance, such that a relatively small change in the solar radiation, or in cloudiness, might have serious consequences for the world's climates. And in recent times man's alteration of the earth's surface, and his injection of larger and larger amounts of waste heat and chemicals into the atmosphere and ocean, raises the real possibility that he may already be changing the climate, possibly in irreversible and undesirable ways.

PAST CLIMATIC CHANGES

That the climate is also capable of changing on shorter time scales is well known. The winter of 1972-1973, for example, was very cool and wet in the western United States and relatively mild and dry in the eastern United States. It was also an unusually warm winter in the Ukraine, which had a direct effect on the wheat harvest produced in that region. Nearly every year produces notable changes in weather in one part of the world or another. Were these changes to persist from year to year they would constitute a change of climate, of which the present widespread drought in West Africa is an example.

Looking further back, we know that since about 1940 the average temperature of the Northern Hemisphere has been slowly falling. This change has now amounted to a cooling of approximately one degree Fahrenheit. We also know that during the period from about 1890 to 1940 the Northern Hemisphere underwent a gradual warming of over 1.5 degrees Fahrenheit. Doubtless such oscillations have occurred in the more distant past, long before instrumental observations have been available to record them. The causes of such widespread warming and cooling trends are not known, although there has been a good deal of speculation.

If we look even further back in time, we know from historical records and from various indirect data sources that the period around 1000 A.D. was one of unusual warmth in the North Atlantic and European region, and that this period of relatively mild winters lasted for several hundred years. This has been called the climatic optimum, and coincides with the period of Viking settlement and exploration of Greenland and North America. Looking even further back, the earth has experienced at least four ice ages in the last quarter million years. The last of these began to fill the Great Lakes as "puddles" some 17,000 years ago as the ice retreated and melted. Sea level at this time was estimated to be some 250 feet lower than it is today, and Asia and North America were connected by a land bridge. The possibilities that this suggests for the spread of animal species and of early man himself have been the subject of much attention.

THE PHYSICAL BASIS OF CLIMATE

The study of climate presents us with an extraordinarily complex physical system. The atmosphere, of course, is involved on all scales from the smallest local variations to the large-scale circulations of the atmosphere as a whole. The world's oceans are also very much in the picture. It has long been recognized, for example, that the warm water currents exert a major influence on the climates of the middle and higher latitudes of the Northern Hemisphere. The oceans supply a great deal of heat to the atmosphere, and are the ultimate source of the moisture that later falls as rain. The earth's surface is also involved through its elevation and its character, whether desert, ice-covered, or forested. The seasonal appearance and disappearance of snow and the semipermanent presence of glaciers and sea ice are also thought to be important components of the climatic physical system.

So all four media—air, water, earth, and ice—are involved in an intricate system of feedbacks, which is what makes the study of climatic change so complex. If man is ever to control climate, or even to forecast the course of climatic variations, either natural or of his own making, he certainly must have a deeper understanding of these interactions. We have today only the barest outline of how parts of this system work, and only a few of the important physical processes have had adequate study.

Climatologists classify the climates in the world principally on the basis of the seasonal regimes of temperature and rainfall. On such a scheme, there are perhaps two dozen climatic classifications or zones that are spread over the continental and oceanic regions of the globe. A primary goal of research is to synthesize this global distribution of climate from first principles, by solving the equations of the complex physical system that govern the behavior of the atmosphere and ocean.

In particular, we would like to know what the climate distributions were during the history of the earth, as well as what they might be in the future. Although our ignorance of the forces controlling climatic changes should make us cautious in projecting future climates, time may be short, and the stakes are certainly very high. Without a theory of climate, we cannot gauge the consequences of the interference of man with his environment, and it is urgent that we acquire such understanding before the climatic system is irreversibly upset.

The physical basis of climate may also be viewed in terms of a global heat engine, in which the atmosphere-ocean-ice-land system responds to the receipt of radiant energy from the sun. In the long run the atmosphere maintains a near balance of radiation, with the short-wave (or solar) radiation entering the atmosphere offset by an equal amount of outgoing long-wave (or infrared) radiation.

But what the atmosphere, ocean, land, and ice do with the energy they receive is less well known. Some of the incoming radiation is scattered by the gaseous molecules of the atmosphere, and this accounts for the apparent blueness of the sky. On its way through the atmosphere, a large portion of the radiation may also be reflected or absorbed by clouds. The clouds are thus an important factor in determining the amount of radiation that enters and leaves the system. The atmosphere is also warmed by the release of latent heat when water vapor condenses into clouds.

The earth's surface itself also affects the disposition of energy. Highly reflective surfaces, such as snow or ice, may reflect as much as 80 percent of the incoming radiation. But a poorly reflecting surface, such as water, reflects only about 8 to 10 percent of the incoming radiation, and absorbs the rest. The oceans are therefore very efficient absorbers of energy from the sun, and, in fact, absorb most of the solar energy falling on the planet earth. The oceans use most of this energy to evaporate water and to heat the atmosphere by direct conduction, and thus act as a vast thermal reservoir.

CLIMATIC FEEDBACK EFFECTS

The problem, however, is a bit more complicated than indicated by the examination of energy alone. As the atmosphere is heated by the sun, differences of temperature are created between regions receiving different amounts of radiation. These cause pressure differences, which then result in winds. The winds, in turn, move the air and thus change the local temperature. So we have a temperature-wind feedback process with the winds themselves braked by friction. This process is illustrated in Fig. 1, along with other components of the climatic system.

In the oceans a similar effect occurs, but with a further interaction between the temperature of the ocean and that of the air. For example, when the water is warmer than the air, heat will leave the ocean and go into the atmosphere as already noted. This occurs off the east coasts of North America and Asia every winter, when enormous amounts of heat are surrendered by the warm Gulf Stream and Kuroshio currents.

Another linkage between air and sea is the winds' effect on the ocean currents themselves. The surface wind acts to drive or push the water, and is a primary cause of the circulation of the world's oceans.

Other climatic feedbacks or interactions concern clouds. We previously mentioned that the clouds intercept radiation, both from the sun and from the earth, and are therefore important in that balance. But the clouds themselves are the results of evaporation and condensation of water vapor, and under certain conditions—not yet completely understood—the cloud droplets will coalesce and precipitate. When the precipitation falls as snow on the land, it whitens the surface and changes the albedo (the surface's reflective power), and yet another feedback mechanism is introduced, as sketched in Fig. 1.

The patterns of heating and cooling that are set up in the atmosphere and in the ocean result in a large-scale pattern of circulation. In general, the low latitudes receive more heat than they surrender, and they are therefore usually warmer than other regions of the earth. It is to the rising of this warmer air that the equatorial and tropical regions owe their generally heavy rainfall. At the same time the polar regions of the world surrender more heat than they receive from the sun.

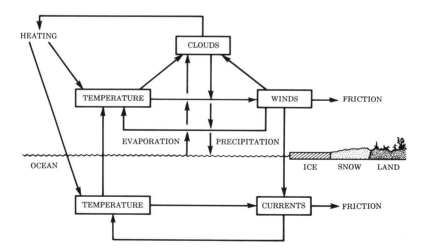

Fig. 1. A simplified sketch of the major components of climate, in which the arrows represent a physical process or interaction.

We can thus envisage a general scheme of circulation, with warm air moving upward and northward from low latitudes, and cooler air generally sinking and moving toward the equator. These two loops of the circulation meet in mid-latitudes and result in the storms or cyclones familiar to us on the daily weather map. These storms, with their associated patterns of wind, temperature, cloudiness, and rainfall, are in fact unstable disturbances, and owe their origin directly to the convergence of the warm and cold air streams. Moving generally from west to east, and also somewhat northward, these high- and low-pressure systems help to transport heat from the tropics to the polar regions.

MATHEMATICAL MODELS

Over the past 20 years, meteorologists have focused attention on the quantitative study of these mid-latitude weather disturbances, and we now understand some of their behavior. By applying this knowledge in the construction of mathematical models, we have achieved a fair degree of success in what is called numerical weather prediction—that is, the numerical solution, on a high-speed computer, of the equations describing these storms. When properly designed, these models can be made to yield useful forecasts for the wind, temperature, pressure, and rainfall, and are routinely used by the National Weather Service.

Unfortunately, we cannot extend these solutions as far ahead as we wish and still have useful accuracy left; at the present time such numerical forecasts are useful for only about 2 days. This limitation on the accuracy of weather forecasting arises from the highly complex character of the atmospheric system, and the lack of understanding of all the interacting components. Even with complete knowledge, however, the inevitable errors in the numerical calculations themselves would sooner or later render the prediction inaccurate.

This is what meteorologists have come to call the "predictability limit," and it refers to our inherent inability to say exactly what the local weather will be for an indefinite period into the future. It now looks as though this limit of predictability lies at about 2 weeks' time, beyond which we cannot ever expect to be able to forecast the weather.

If such a situation exists for short-range forecasts, what hope is there then in forecasting longer-range changes such as must be involved in climate? Our hope is that while we cannot tell what the changes may be in a particular place on a particular day, we may very well be able to say something of the average character of the weather, which is, after all, the definition of climate. Very simplified models indicate that a small change in the sun's radiation, for example, may be able to cause glaciation of the entire earth. We obviously want to check such a prediction with the best models available, and thus to move toward the development of a more complete theory of climate.

Broadly speaking, the synthesis of just such a theory of climate is the goal of the Rand Climate Dynamics Project. We are using mathematical models of the atmosphere as our primary tool because they offer the only comprehensive framework within which to study the interacting components of climate. Our climatic experiments to date have used a Rand-modified version of a model originally developed at the University of California at Los Angeles. With this model we have simulated the average state of the atmosphere over periods of 1 or 2 months under a variety of imposed conditions. By comparing the distributions of temperature, pressure, wind, and rainfall obtained from this numerical model with those actually observed in the atmosphere, we can then determine how well the climate has been depicted.

In general, we find that the large-scale distribution of pressure over the globe is reasonably well simulated. The semistationary high-pressure regions are rather well reproduced over the subtropical oceans, for example, whereas the average low-pressure areas near Iceland and the Aleutians are generally simulated with too great an intensity. This as well as other features may be seen in the simulated and observed January sea-level pressure distributions shown in Fig. 2.

In addition to pressure, the model predicts the worldwide distributions of temperature and wind at two levels in the atmosphere, together with the cloudiness, precipitation,

OBSERVED SEA-LEVEL PRESSURE

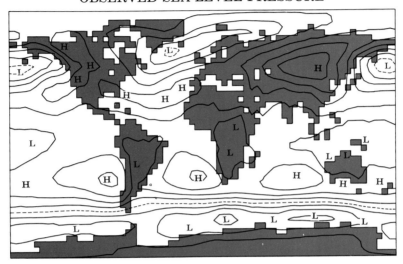

SIMULATED SEA-LEVEL PRESSURE

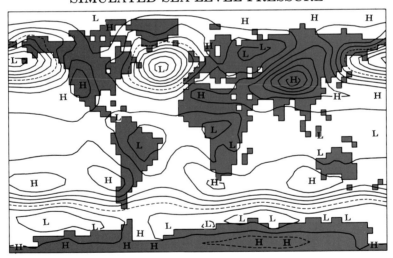

Fig. 2. The observed and simulated distributions of January
sea-level pressure. The isobars are drawn every 5 mb in each case,
with the 1000-mb line dashed. The shaded regions denote the
world's land areas as seen by the network of grid points used in
the numerical model.

evaporation, and heat balance at the earth's surface. The resemblance of these simulated climatic elements to those observed is generally satisfactory, although there is evidence of systematic errors in the model.

Of these, the case of rainfall is particularly prominent. In our calculations (for the month of January) we successfully produce rain in the equatorial and tropical regions, but unfortunately the calculated rainfall is about twice that observed. This miscalculation is related to the difficulty of accurately portraying the rainfall that occurs during local convective showers, as the model cannot "see" such small-scale features. A similar error occurs in other numerical models of the atmosphere, such as the nine-level model in use at the National Oceanic and Atmospheric Administration Laboratories in Princeton, and the six-level model in use at the National Center for Atmospheric Research in Boulder, Colorado.

CLIMATIC CHANGE EXPERIMENTS AND RESEARCH

Such comparisons with the observed climate have given us enough confidence in the overall fidelity of the model that we have felt justified in proceeding with a program of numerical experiments on climatic change. In these experiments we deliberately make changes in the distribution of the ocean temperature or in the incoming radiation, for example, and seek to discover the consequences in terms of climate.

In one such experiment we have reduced the solar radiation by a few percent, and have found the expected cooling in the simulated atmosphere. By the end of a 60-day integration, we have not been able to identify any climatic changes that appear to presage an ice age, although, as I have mentioned, some theories indicate that such an event would eventually occur were the sun's radiation permanently reduced in this way.

In another experiment we have changed the temperature of the ocean's surface in the North Pacific to represent the pools of anomalously warm water observed in recent years in this region. This change increased the evaporation and heat flux into the air over the North Pacific, and lowered the pressure in the Gulf of Alaska. These in turn affected the heat balance and cloudiness so as to raise the air temperature over the eastern North Pacific by several degrees at the end of two months' time. Extension of such experiments to longer time periods would allow us to examine the influence of this warmer-than-normal Pacific on the winter weather of the eastern United States. A connection between the two has been hypothesized, and the ocean may be a key factor in causing such seasonal climatic changes.

One of the difficulties in numerical climatic experiments of this sort is determining just what is significant and what is not. We mentioned earlier the lack of predictability present in the weather forecasting problem, and made the hypothesis that there might nevertheless be some predictability in the long-term averages. There does appear to be some, but we are not entirely free of the problems that plague the weather forecaster. It seems that any small change—whether it represents a deliberate change of boundary condition (such as sea-surface temperature) or an uncertainty in the data at some point—can to some extent generate anomalies of simulated climate.

For example, if you were to make an experiment in which the only alteration was to change the data in the last decimal at one location in the world, the 30-day averaged solution from an atmospheric model would differ from the one you would have found without the change. They would not be greatly different, to be sure, but the changes of wind and temperature would be several miles per hour and several degrees Fahrenheit in scattered regions around the world.

Your problem would be to find those regions, if any, in which you could state with confidence that you had made a significant change, and which changes were just the reflection of the inevitable "noise" level in the model. If your experiment was indeed only the alteration of the last decimal in a quantity, you would have no expectation that you had significantly changed the climate. But if your experiment had involved, say, large changes of the albedo over the whole globe or the removal of all mountains from the North American continent, you would have an expectation of climatic change.

Thus a major problem now being researched is how to deal with this uncertainty in solutions from models with a limited predictability, so that we may focus on what could be called true climatic changes.

In addition to this question of experiment analysis, research must be directed to those aspects of the models that are deficient. We have mentioned the problem of convection, which results from so much tropical rainfall. The atmosphere's interaction with the underlying sea is a second important problem, and efforts to include the ocean circulation in the climatic system are under way at Rand as elsewhere. This will raise the level of complexity (and hopefully also the realism) of future climatic experiments.

A third important research area has to do with the boundary layer of the atmosphere. This is a layer very close to the earth's surface, through which heat is transferred to the air and through which most of the air's energy is in turn lost by turbulent friction. Like convection, this feature is not resolved in climatic models and must be represented in a parametric or indirect way.

We must also recognize that the one- or two-month long experiments we have been discussing are not true climatic calculations. January climate, after all, is not just one January, but the average of many Januaries. If we are to make meaningful statements of the effects of this or that change in the atmospheric system upon climate, we must carry our calculations out for at least several years.

This is very expensive in terms of computer time, and will require access to very high speed and high capacity computers. We are fortunate in having access scheduled for such a computer—the ILLIAC IV—now being installed at the Ames Research Center near San Francisco. Through the sponsorship of the Defense Advanced Research Projects Agency, we are looking forward to the performance of climatic experiments of several years' length on this machine. With an interacting ocean and with improved representations for both convection and the boundary layer, we hope to be able to answer, at least partially, the questions of whether the variations of ocean temperature, ice cover, or solar radiation do indeed represent significant climatic controls.

OUTLOOK FOR THE FUTURE

Looking ahead, we might ask to what extent will it ever be possible to predict the climatic consequences of given environmental changes. If we were to load the atmosphere with dust, for example, or to remove the Arctic sea ice, what long-term effects would this have on the world's climates? What long-term climatic effects would the global operation of a fleet of high-altitude supersonic transports have? And what will happen as man continues to clear forests, to pollute the atmosphere, and to emit waste heat from his expanding energy consumption?

If we can acquire the outline of a theory of climate by a research program such as the one described here, I believe it will be possible in the future to specify beforehand what the climatic consequences of such actions will be, or at least to put limits on the consequences.

Looking even further ahead, we might well ask whether or not another ice age is coming. Or will there be anything we can do about it if we decide it is coming? These are harder questions, but they, too, will likely succumb to continued research, and provide man with a measure of both climatic engineering and climatic forecasting. The stakes are high and the prospect is a worthy challenge.

ABOUT THE AUTHOR: W. Lawrence Gates is Leader of Rand's Climate Dynamics Project, sponsored by the Defense Advanced Research Projects Agency. After receiving his doctorate in meteorology from the Massachusetts Institute of Technology in 1955, he served as research meteorologist and director of the Numerical Prediction Project at Air Force Cambridge Research Center until 1957. Coming to California, he took a professorship at the University of California at Los Angeles and in 1966 joined the Rand staff. Dr. Gates has been a leader in developing numerical prediction methods—methods that apply the power of digital computers—in both meteorology and oceanography.

... the benefits and the costs to society of technological advance over time may be far more important than the objective of maintaining rates....

Government Regulation and Technological Advance

Leland L. Johnson

Government regulation has become a pervasive force in American private industry. Regulation typically has one or more conscious objectives: to control price and the quality of service for industries not subject to normal competitive checks and balances; to assure the provision of service considered essential to the public welfare; to protect the public against fraud and misrepresentation on the one hand, and damage to the physical environment on the other. But the *consequences* of regulation transcend these objectives, and should be taken into account in evaluating its impact.

One important consequence is the effect regulation has on the development and assimilation of new technology. The purpose of this essay is to suggest how regulation can affect technological advance, and to draw some inferences for public policy.

THE REGULATORY PROCESS

The most pervasive rationale for regulation is the alleged need to counteract "natural" monopoly power of public utilities and large entities in the transportation and communications fields. The federal regulatory commissions and state public utilities commissions seek to ensure that rates to consumers as well as profits to private firms be held to reasonable levels.

The second basis for regulation—assuring the provision of services essential to the public welfare—assumes that if we relied solely on the private market mechanism, either the public would be charged inordinately high prices for services or the service would not be offered at all. This viewpoint is reflected typically by insistence on "internal subsidization." Airlines, for example, may be forced to serve small cities at a loss, with losses recovered through profits on high-density (and profitable) routes. And the telephone industry is forced to serve rural areas at rates considered to be relatively unprofitable while the burden for profits falls on the metropolitan markets.

The third basis for regulation—protection—is reflected in the many safety and health regulations imposed by federal, state, and local agencies; the laws against fraud and misrepresentation, such as the federal Truth in Lending Act; and, especially important in recent years, the numerous regulations and restrictions intended to safeguard the environment.

To appraise the effect of regulation on technological advance, we distinguish between two kinds of industries: (1) those that operate in reaction to free market forces and are subject to a minimum of regulatory controls (as in safety and health), and (2) those that constitute natural monopolies, where the regulatory process is widespread. In the first category, government regulations impose few constraints on the firm's activities, and so the effect of controls on technological advance is not of special concern. (In the future, however, progressively more stringent controls in environment and safety may affect the course of technological advance in these industries.)

In the second category—firms typically in the fields of communications and transportation and the public utilities—regulatory commissions have the power both to force rate decreases and to permit rate increases; to disapprove abandonment of service; to require certificates of "public convenience and necessity" before a firm can offer new services or invest in new major facilities; and, as mentioned above, to force a firm to offer unprofitable services as a form of internal or "cross" subsidization, allegedly in the public interest. The effect on technological advance is especially important here, since these heavily regulated industries accounted for nearly 40 percent of new plant and equipment investment by U.S. private industry in 1972.

We now consider three major links between regulatory processes and technological advance: (1) the role of rate-base regulation, (2) the effect of price control, and (3) specific responses of regulatory agencies to new technologies and services.

THE ROLE OF RATE-BASE REGULATION

How public commissions apply the rate-making process is a prime factor in the relationship between regulation and technological advance. The basic criterion is "a fair rate of return on investment." Net revenues to the firm, less allowable costs of operation, are computed as a percentage of the firm's net assets or "rate base." If this percentage return exceeds a level considered to be "fair" (such as 8 percent annually), rates to consumers are judged to be excessive. If net revenues fall below this fair level, the firm is permitted to raise rates.

This process can have both negative and positive effects on technological advance. For example, a firm would be reluctant to continue developing new technology if such technology reduced capital expenditures, thereby cutting into the rate base that determines the firm's level of permitted profits. Also, if costs were reduced as a consequence of new technology, and the regulatory agency immediately required a commensurate rate decrease to consumers, the firm would forgo its profits. Thus, it would have no incentive to cut costs.

In reality, the problem of cost reductions is mitigated by the effects of "regulatory lag." Only after a series of prolonged hearings and other procedural steps in the rate-making process are cost decreases met with rate reductions. In the interim, the firm is often permitted to keep the extra profits. The positive incentives of regulatory lag have led some economists to suggest that the decisionmaking process be deliberately geared to provide for such time lapses.

Inflationary pressures, so prevalent today, represent another mitigating factor that works in combination with regulatory lag. When costs rise, permitted rate increases decline, again because of procedural steps. The firm caught in a cost-price squeeze is motivated to pursue new technology in order to cut costs and reduce pressures on dwindling profits.

As another stimulant to technological advance, R&D expenditures can be written off with other "allowable" operating costs to arrive at the net revenue figure for computing the fair rate of return. A firm that engages in R&D activities can avoid accumulating excess profits. However, this practice could stimulate R&D expenditures beyond reasonable bounds and even encourage wasteful expenses.

Beyond these theoretical considerations, we should note how, in fact, heavily regulated industries rank with others in terms of productivity changes over time. One major study suggests that these industries have generally done well. During a fifty-year period, communications, public utilities, and transportation all led private domestic industry as a whole in growth of labor and capital productivity. Electric utilities have achieved especially impressive gains.

However, a simple comparison of productivity changes in regulated and nonregulated industry doesn't tell us whether regulation has had deleterious effects on technological advance. A number of factors operate in addition to new technology in bringing about changes in productivity over such a long time span. Also, regulation by itself could have either positive and negative effects.

These conflicting considerations make it impossible to quantify the net effect of rate-base regulation. In both camps we find progressive industries and unprogressive industries. The telephone and electric utility industries, which are subject to rate-base regulation, have shown solid gains—as well as the computer field, which has been free of such control. Advances in rail passenger traffic, also subject to rate-base regulation, have lagged, and so has residential construction, which is outside of the regulated field. Many factors are at work, including the expansion or contraction of markets, breakthroughs in particular fields (as in the invention of the transistor) that have had widespread effects in both regulated and unregulated sectors, labor union practices, and the nature of competitive forces. The effects we are seeking get lost in the static.

THE ROLE OF PRICE CONTROL

A second link between public-utility-type regulation and technological advance relates to particular forms of price control in the hands of public authorities, in addition to *overall* price control grounded in rate-base regulation. Here also price control can have both positive and negative effects.

In the positive direction, we can draw an example from the airlines. The Civil Aeronautics Board has been reluctant to permit price competition among airlines. Hence, the airlines have had to resort to other measures: better food, service, and other amenities, and the best of new aircraft. Competition for new and better aircraft has undoubtedly stimulated technological advance in this industry. In fact, some writers have conjectured that the rate of technological advance has been too fast; that in order to stay in the race airlines have been forced to buy new and expensive equipment they could ill afford.

In contrast, consider the pricing policies by the Interstate Commerce Commission with respect to piggyback rail freight. Although a railcar designed with a single truck trailer container is a less costly solution for many railroads, the imposition of minimum revenue requirements on a per-freight-car basis by the ICC has encouraged the railroads to go to a more costly two-container railcar design.

Another example is the Federal Power Commission's maximum price control of natural gas field prices. The rationale for price ceilings has been that a rise in prices would not increase the supply of gas but would merely increase the profits of field operators (a rationale that is increasingly being challenged today in view of the growing problem of energy supply). The extent to which such price ceilings have tended to retard technological advance in the production of natural gas remains an open question.

There are many more examples of how price control *might* have affected technological advance, in one direction or another, but the problem, once again, is to isolate regulatory effects from the other factors that influence the behavior of regulated and nonregulated industries.

REGULATORY RESPONSE TO NEW TECHNOLOGIES AND SERVICES

A third approach in exploring relationships between regulatory processes and technological advance is to examine how regulatory agencies have coped with the development and assimilation of specific major technological advances. At one extreme, we see advances that were assimilated with little fuss and fanfare. These advances (1) permitted development of new services without discriminating against or shutting out users who were dependent on the outmoded technologies; and (2) were introduced by the same firms that were using the older technologies.

A leading example was the introduction of transoceanic telephone cable in the mid-1950s as a substitute for radiotelephone service. The substitution of cable was easy because it did not adversely affect service to those users who remained dependent on radiotelephone over international routes where service by cable was uneconomic. Radiotelephone service continues to be provided to isolated points, and at rates no higher than those that would have prevailed had transoceanic cable not been developed. Moreover, the firms that introduced transoceanic cable, both in the United States and abroad, were the same as those that controlled radiotelephone facilities.

A second example was the introduction of jet airliners. Passengers dependent on propeller aircraft continued to be served over short, low-density routes not suitable for jet aircraft. And again the airlines that introduced jet aircraft were the ones that had been using the earlier technology.

In both of these cases, regulatory agencies were able to take the advances well in stride. There were no serious problems with new firms seeking entry into markets dominated by firms tied to the older technologies, and no immediate pressure from special-interest groups that might be threatened by the new technologies.

There are, however, many examples of advances that have had adverse service effects and have posed problems of pressures from competing firms. The development of the airline industry had a severe impact on rail passenger traffic, and for years this service limped along, subsidized by freight revenues. The situation became progressively less tenable as losses continued to mount. Rather than permit the bulk of intercity rail passenger traffic to be abandoned, thus harming those who were dependent on rail transportation, the government responded by establishing AMTRAK, through which subsidies amounting to nearly $148 million in 1972 were poured into rail passenger traffic. Of interest here is that the development of aircraft technology was not deliberately retarded to protect rail passenger traffic; rather, public subsidy was eventually brought to bear to support the threatened industry.

In contrast to the airline-rail example is cable television, whose development has been retarded, at least until recently, to protect over-the-air broadcasting. Cable television, it was feared, would bring large numbers of outside television signals into markets where hitherto only a few television stations operated, and would erode the revenues of television stations, reducing their quality of service and even driving them off the air. Viewers having access to so-called free television (supported in fact by advertiser sponsorship) would consequently be forced to pay the $5 or so per month for subscription to cable.

In response, the Federal Communications Commission decided in the late 1960s to prohibit cable systems in major metropolitan areas from carrying outside signals in competition with local broadcasting stations. After long reconsideration, the FCC decided in 1972 to permit cable systems to bring a few outside signals into major markets as a compromise—one that would stimulate growth of cable television and yet not pose a serious threat to over-the-air broadcasting.

In comparing the development of cable television and the airline industry, we find that the growth of cable was retarded to protect an existing service, whereas the airlines were permitted to grow in competition with another mode, and with the government eventually providing a subsidy to support the endangered service. The difference here may be that in the case of cable and broadcasting a single regulatory agency had jurisdiction over the two competing modes, and therefore had to choose between them. In the case of the airlines and railroads, *two* regulatory agencies were involved—the Civil Aeronautics Board and the Interstate Commerce Commission—each with its own objectives of promoting and protecting the industries under its purview.

The problems of a single regulatory agency coping with technological advances offered by competing firms are also evident in the communications satellite and transoceanic cable industries. Early in the development of communications satellites, the Communication Satellite Corporation (COMSAT) was formed to provide satellite services for international use. At the same time, traffic served by transoceanic cable remained with the existing telecommunications common carriers. (For the United States, these include AT&T and several international telegraph or "record" carriers.)

The FCC decided that COMSAT would be prohibited from offering end-to-end service to final users at the "retail" level but rather would be restricted to leasing its channels as a wholesaler or middleman to AT&T and to the record carriers who were to serve final users. The sale of satellite services was thus made dependent on the carriers' choice of facilities. Because terrestrial carriers have preferred continued construction of their own facilities to leasing channels from COMSAT, the development of communications satellites has been handicapped. A subject of bitter debate in recent years has been the roles that cable and satellites should play in response to varying market conditions, establishing route structures, and combining facilities to ensure adequate overall service reliability.

To illustrate, in 1967-1968 authorization for a new transoceanic cable between the United States and Spain was challenged on whether the increase in capacity could not better be obtained through the use of additional satellites. After a long debate, the FCC allowed the construction of the new cable. Within the last year, a similar debate has been waged about the construction of another transoceanic cable—and again the FCC finally authorized its construction.

A further problem to regulatory agencies is the new firm that attempts to serve only the most lucrative routes in competition with established firms—a form of "cream skimming." For many years communications firms have sought to compete with AT&T and other existing carriers by offering new kinds of voice and data services reflecting technological advances in long-distance transmission and in terminal equipment. Early in the game, the FCC prohibited such competitive entry to protect established carriers and prevent them from having to increase rates in rural and other less profitable markets to make up losses.

Again, only after bitter debate did the FCC authorize competitive entry, allowing the new firms to skim the best markets. Today several specialized carriers—the first, MCI

(Microwave Communications of America, Inc.), operating
between St. Louis and Chicago—have ambitious plans to offer
service among major cities.

IMPLICATIONS FOR PUBLIC POLICY

There appears to be no basis to suggest radical modifications
in the *rate-base approach* to regulation of technological
advance in industry. Arguments can be posed on both sides
and, as we have seen, the regulated industries have together
done relatively well in showing increases in productivity over
time.

Regulatory agencies need to consider more seriously what
effect *price control* has on technological advance; decisions by
firms may be distorted by higher cost technologies, as in the
piggyback rail case or, at the other extreme, technological
advance may be accelerated beyond that which is socially
desirable. In both cases, the benefits and the costs to society of
technological advance over time may be far more important
than the objective of maintaining rates that, in a static
framework, are considered reasonable.

On the issue of *intrafirm versus competing-firm behavior,* we
have seen that technological advance may be easiest to
assimilate when the firm is in control of both the old and new
technologies. But will the firm with this degree of control, and
without competitive stimulus, have the incentive to develop
and introduce new technologies when needed? On one hand,
competition is recognized as an important stimulus to
technological advance; on the other, regulatory agencies face
problems of "cream skimming" and adverse service
displacement when firms are allowed to compete.

To what extent should particular services be protected from
competitive forces? We lack valid criteria by which to judge
the importance to the public of endangered services (such as
rail passenger traffic). Another problem is which method of
support to choose for those services considered vital, on
whatever basis, to the public interest. Should they be
supported by internal subsidization, with the firm forced to
compensate losses from profits gained in its more lucrative

markets? Or should the services be protected by prohibiting or retarding the growth of competing technologies? Or should they be supported by public subsidy, in the face of competing technologies that are permitted to develop freely in accordance with their own potential?

Although the answers vary from case to case, there are several reasons for choosing the route of public subsidy (if subsidy in *any* form is justifiable). First, the true burden on the society supporting such services is made more clear (as with AMTRAK) since the subsidy can be quantified. A problem with internal subsidy is that the burden on society is clouded—the degree of support is not made clear from company records, which tend to lump together services, costs, and revenues into common accounts.

Second, by using public subsidy, it is easier to permit competitive entry and "cream skimming" to stimulate technological advance, which benefits those in the more lucrative markets, and perhaps in the longer run those in the less lucrative markets, through technological "spillover." The jet airliner is a good example. Originally, it was practical only over long-distance, high-density routes, as between Los Angeles and New York; but now, with the continued development of jet aircraft engines and airframes, it is becoming increasingly profitable to serve low-density, shorter routes.

Finally, should industries be grouped under the jurisdiction of a *single* regulatory agency or under several? With many industries and their technologies under a single regulatory umbrella, the agency may be tempted to retard the growth of one industry in favor of another. With several regulatory agencies, each pursuing its own objectives, a potentially more healthy competitive situation may emerge in industry and technology. Here, as in so many other areas, the evidence is scant. But the issue of regulatory jurisdiction is one that merits close attention in future policymaking.

ABOUT THE AUTHOR: Leland Johnson, Director of Rand's Communications Policy Program, has been with Rand since

1957. An economist by training (Ph.D., Yale), Dr. Johnson participated extensively in Rand research on military R&D policy and the economics of commercial communications satellite systems. Under a Rand contract with the State Department, he spent a year in Chile examining the balance of payments problem and the most useful forms of U.S. assistance. In 1967, after contributing to major Ford Foundation recommendations on the future domestic satellite industry, he was asked by the White House to serve as research director of the President's Task Force on Communications Policy to consider how the radio, telephone, and television industries should be regulated. His most recent publications have been in the cable television field.

... Soviet doctrine represents a mandate for endless competition without defined standards of what constitutes enough....

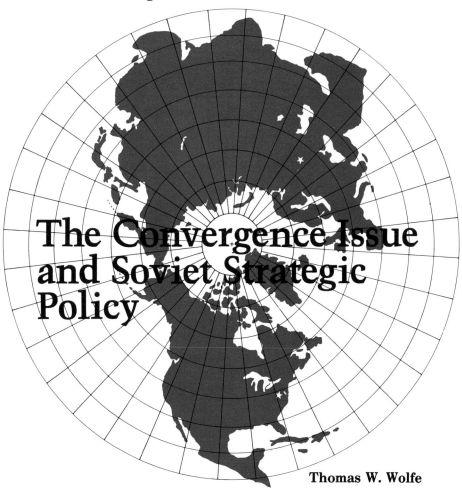

The Convergence Issue and Soviet Strategic Policy

Thomas W. Wolfe

Today one frequently encounters the view that the Soviet Union's effort of the past decade to achieve strategic equality with the United States has been paralleled by increasing convergence in the strategic philosophies of the two sides. As the Soviet Union has caught up in strategic forces with its once markedly superior rival, so its strategic thinking and policy are presumed to have moved closer to the example set by the United States.

In a sense, the concept of "strategic convergence" can be regarded as a logical offshoot of a broader school of convergence thought, which holds that the processes of industrialization, modernization, and societal change will gradually bring the American and Soviet systems closer together, eroding the deeper sources of past antagonism between them and making it easier to find common ground for accommodation of their conflicting interests. Similarly, strategic convergence is looked upon in some quarters as a phenomenon that should improve the prospects of regulating competition between the United States and the Soviet Union in the strategic arena, through the medium of the SALT talks and other negotiations.

The present essay is intended to explore several questions arising from the convergence issue. What factors help to account for the belief that Soviet strategic policy and practices are on a convergent path with those of the United States? To what extent have convergent tendencies been offset by significant points of divergence in the strategic philosophies of the two sides? How valid is the thesis that accelerated Soviet-American interaction in SALT over the past three years has already produced a fundamental convergence of strategic outlook? And finally, whatever may be said with regard to these matters, what implications appear to flow therefrom for the future course of Soviet strategic policy?

RATIONALE OF THE STRATEGIC CONVERGENCE THESIS

To begin with, it must be recognized that the strategic relationship between the United States and the Soviet Union has not evolved in a vacuum, untouched by either external changes in the international environment or by such internal factors as economic pressures, bureaucratic politics, vested interests, and manipulative leadership personalities. Without trying at this point to trace the intricate interplay of external and internal influences that have helped to shape the strategic policies of both sides, one can identify several factors contributing to the general belief that these policies are now on a convergent path.

First, there is the circumstance that the whole pattern of world politics today is in a state of flux. The familiar lines of bipolar rivalry between the Soviet Union and the United States are being displaced by a more complex and diverse pattern of international alignments. To put it another way, the period of attempted postwar containment of the Soviet Union has come to an end, but the rules of engagement under which the USSR and the United States will deal with their overlapping global interests and conflicts in an increasingly multipolar world environment are still in the process of being worked out.

In this transitional situation, which can be viewed as a stage in a broader historical process of redefining the overall political and power relationship between the Soviet Union and the United States, the two superpowers appear to share at least one strong motivation in common: to conduct their contest for power and influence in the world so as to avoid the risk of war with each other. Precisely because today's global environment is in a fluid transitional stage, fraught with the uncertainties that attend a reordering of the international system of the past quarter-century, this common motivation may serve all the more to impel both sides to display a scrupulous regard for the way their strategic policies are perceived by the other. This in itself would mark a large step toward mutuality of outlook and strategic convergence—or so it can be argued.

A second circumstance to be noted is the present recourse of the Soviet leadership to détente and negotiation as the modality of Soviet policy, rather than to the confrontation tactics sometimes practiced in the past. This is not precisely what had been anticipated for a Soviet Union operating from a power position more favorable than it has ever enjoyed before. A more subtle Soviet performance may simply attest to a good learning curve from past experience, in which pressure tactics often had the effect of prompting the West to close its ranks. Nevertheless, coming as a counterpart to the American suggestion that an era of confrontation should give way to an era of negotiation, this more pliable mode of Soviet behavior can be taken to mean that despite the growth of Soviet strategic power assets relative to those of the United States, the prospect for convergent thinking on how to stabilize the strategic relationship between the two has perceptibly improved.

Third, the action-reaction model often employed to describe the Soviet-American strategic competition has contributed to a view that convergent tendencies are inherent in this competition. In this view, Soviet policies and programs have been essentially reactive to American moves in the strategic field, where—owing to the historical headstart of the United States—the Soviet Union faced the problem of catching up and hence tended to follow imitatively the path taken by its strategically superior adversary. Close scrutiny of the interaction process would suggest that it is a far more complex phenomenon than this rendition implies, and that Soviet decisionmakers probably have marched to the tune of their own political dynamic and strategic doctrine no less than they have followed the American example. However, to the extent that the Soviet side has been the emulative party in the strategic competition, the implication remains that, allowing for a certain amount of lag time, one might logically expect the Soviet Union's postural and doctrinal steps to converge with those of its preceptor.

Fourth, but not least among the factors that have contributed to the strategic convergence school of thought, is the SALT experience of the past three years. Though by no means a universally held view, it is widely believed that the SALT I agreements of May 1972, especially the ABM Treaty, capped a process of convergence in the strategic philosophies and practices of the two sides—at the heart of which supposedly lies recognition by both parties that deterrence and strategic stability can best be achieved by what is known in the American strategic lexicon as the concept of "mutual assured destruction."

Such, then, is the general thrust of the strategic convergence thesis. At this point, let it be said that while it may be eminently desirable for the Soviet Union and the United States to pursue strategic policies tuned to the same wavelength, so to speak, it would appear more than a little premature to assert that this has already taken place. What are the grounds for such a judgment?

POINTS OF DIVERGENCE IN STRATEGIC PHILOSOPHIES

One should recognize at the outset that there have been notable areas of convergence over the course of time between U.S. and Soviet strategic conceptions and practices, in part perhaps because of certain basic symmetries in the advanced military technology that has become the common property of both sides. For example, in addition to treating deterrence as a high-priority function of their strategic forces, both have moved toward protecting these forces through hardening on land and mobility at sea. Both sides have chosen to maintain something akin to a triad of offensive systems in land-based missiles, bombers, and submarine-launched missiles, and both have made starts toward incorporating ABM systems in their strategic defenses.

But such convergent trends also have been offset, if not frequently overshadowed, by persistent divergences in Soviet thinking and practice. These are to be seen, for example, in doctrinal resistance to a "deterrence-only" strategic posture and in the durability of the idea that the Soviet Union should seek "balanced forces," backed by an extensive civil defense system, enabling it to wage war and improve the chances of national survival if deterrence should fail. We shall return to this key question in a moment.

With regard to measures for improving the survivability of strategic forces, some distinct conceptual differences stand out in the Soviet and American cases. In the United States, such measures have been emphasized for their contribution to the stability of deterrence, not only through preserving second-strike forces for "assured destruction" purposes, but also by making it possible to ride out attacks, withhold forces, and respond with less than an all-out nuclear exchange. The Soviet Union, on the other hand, has given these aspects of its hardened and mobile strategic forces scant mention, emphasizing instead a high state of readiness and preparation for the prompt launching of the bulk of its strategic weapons

during an initial nuclear exchange. In particular, the Soviet
side has tended to ignore the U.S. admonition that mutual
survival of offensive forces, not merely the survival of one's
own, is of salient concern.

Another asymmetry between Soviet and American strategic
conceptions shows up in the Soviets' indifference toward the
argument advanced by some schools of thought in the United
States to the effect that one should avoid a strategic posture
that appears to pose a counterforce threat that could make the
opponent feel insecure. Thus, for example, the Soviets have
seen no need to pledge themselves to a design goal of
restricting delivery accuracy, as the United States has done in
recent years, in order to avoid posing a counterforce threat to
the other side. The Soviet attitude toward counterforce, one
should note, does not necessarily imply malign first-strike
intentions, as sometimes charged. By the same token, however,
it is not coupled with the idea that, once both sides have
acquired survivable forces sufficient for assured destruction,
any further investment in counterforce capabilities is at best
wasteful and marginal, or at worst dangerous to stability and
a stimulus to the strategic arms race.

If it is possible to pinpoint the issue on which the American
and Soviet approaches to the realities of strategic nuclear
power have differed most fundamentally, it is probably the
dilemma of deterrence versus war-fighting and survival. This is
a dilemma almost philosophical in nature, but profoundly
practical in its military, political, and economic consequences.

The United States has sought to resolve this dilemma
primarily in favor of deterrence by maintaining a capability to
inflict massive punishment on the society of an attacking
opponent, and conceding the other side the ability to do the
same. The result is the concept of "mutual assured
destruction." Despite institutional pressures for forces that
exceed the assured destruction criterion, it has to date
remained the central axis of consensus around which major
force posture and arms control decisions in the United States
are made. The Soviet Union, on the other hand, while no less
dedicated to deterring a nuclear attack, has proved reluctant
to peg its security to the concept of mutual assured

destruction, dwelling instead on the traditional problems of war-fighting and survival if deterrence should fail.

The conceptual gulf between these two approaches runs deeper than is sometimes appreciated. Without taking the position that the mutual assured destruction concept (described in some quarters by the acronym MAD) is necessarily the most satisfactory answer to the problem of security in the nuclear age, one may note that it does happen to be functionally compatible with both strategic stability and arms control objectives. This is so, essentially, because it is a far less difficult military task to put the opponent's society in jeopardy than to protect one's own. Targets such as cities and population are easy to attack and hard to defend. In effect, the knee of the equivalent megatonnage-fatalities curve* suggests itself as a posturally "sufficient" and conceptually convenient point at which two strategic competitors can come to rest and mutually accommodate—that is, if both accept the idea of living indefinitely with what is customarily described as "the balance of terror."

By contrast, the Soviet strategic philosophy appears functionally incompatible with finding any clear stopping points and striking such an equilibrium. Given the dominance of offensive over defensive technology, and the woeful "softness" of populations, a doctrine that seeks substantial survival levels for one's own society, in addition to assured destruction of the opponent, places before itself seemingly impossible force requirements. As long as this remains its operational goal, therefore, Soviet doctrine represents a mandate for endless competition without defined standards of what constitutes enough—short of massive, damage-limiting superiority, which is probably unachievable unless the adversary quits trying altogether.

Patently, it would be wrong to assert that Soviet strategic policy has been governed only by this driving doctrinal mandate. Many other considerations—economic and technological constraints, institutional factors, diplomatic exigencies—have tempered and shaped the translation of the doctrine into policy. At the same time, however, and despite the demanding character of the doctrine, it is worth noting that both the Soviet military and political leaderships have cause for not lightly discarding it.

In the military case, the reasons are fairly obvious. Psychologically and institutionally, the military professionals find congenial a doctrine that stresses the traditional goals of preparing to defend the country in the ultimate test of war, and that seems to assign them a responsible and meaningful role if such a test should occur. The doctrine is congenial to the military in other respects also, for it gives them a constant claim on the country's best manpower and material resources. Although it does not solve internal controversy over the allocation of resources among service claimants, it does ease their solution through generous defense budgets.

The adherence of the political leadership to what might be called the strategic nuclear traditionalism of the military is, one must assume, more ambivalent. Lacking the institutional stakes of the military in the doctrine, leaders like Brezhnev and others are probably more free to consider the economic benefits of a less demanding strategic philosophy. But they too have their own investment in a doctrinal consensus that calls for more than deterrent sufficiency. The political disadvantages of a deterrence-only philosophy were keenly brought home by Khrushchev's Cuban experience, contributing to the "never again" syndrome displayed by his successors. Their interest in having at their disposal strategic power not only to deter nuclear war, but to help create an environment favorable to achieving Soviet political aims, was underscored by the massive strategic buildup they sanctioned after Khrushchev's removal.

The details of this buildup were left largely to the military professionals, and although it doubtless fell short of meeting the elusive requirements for an adequate war-fighting and survival posture, its political payoff can hardly have failed to impress the Politburo chieftains. For in their eyes, the buildup not only gave the Soviet Union greater room for diplomatic maneuver, but more specifically, it "sobered" the American "imperialists," led them to concede that containment of the USSR was a bankrupt strategy, and impelled them to seek settlement of long-standing issues through negotiation instead of confrontation. In short, by contrast with the fashionable tendency in the West to deprecate the political utility of strategic power, Soviet experience would seem to have confirmed it.

Thus, on both the military and political sides of the house, there appears to be a built-in bias in the Soviet case toward perpetuation of a doctrine that says in effect that further accretion of strategic power makes policy sense, even though it may offer no logical end point for the strategic competition. Such an outlook, should it endure, would certainly seem to pose a major obstacle to the merging of U.S. and Soviet approaches to strategic policy. But, there is SALT to be considered. What, it may be asked, has been the impact of the SALT experience to date on this and other roadblocks to convergence of Soviet and American strategic thinking?

IMPACT OF SALT NEGOTIATIONS

The SALT process clearly has introduced some significant elements into the Soviet-U.S. strategic relationship that did not exist previously when both strategic competitors were essentially free to shape their strategic postures as they saw fit—within the customary constraints imposed by resources, technology, geography, and the like. Besides bringing some measure of "joint" Soviet-American strategic planning into the picture, SALT promises to politicize strategic interaction between the two sides to a greater degree than hitherto, for it has created a political imperative to show that strategic policies are—at the least—not inconsistent with the SALT undertakings.

In the Soviet case, one important consequence may be that many strategic matters which by past Soviet custom were "left to the marshals," as Kosygin once remarked, have now been politicized to the point that will get more intensive scrutiny from the top political leadership. The long give-and-take of the negotiating process itself and the preparation of coordinated papers by backup agencies in Moscow also may have familiarized many middle-echelon Soviet officials with a body of strategic lore hitherto largely the province of the military.

All this can be taken to mean that Soviet officialdom from the top down has been sensitized to previously unperceived subtleties of the strategic relationship and prompted to think in terms of a stabilization of the arms competition for which there has been little place in Soviet strategic doctrine and policy over the past decade. Parenthetically, one might add that the Soviet leaders also could have become more sensitized to the multiplier effect of negotiations on the political value of strategic forces. In an era of bargaining with one's adversary, these forces tend to become the instruments through which gains are won at the negotiating table—a point not likely to have escaped a leadership already persuaded that its investment in strategic power should yield returns beyond deterrence alone.

To return to the question of how SALT may have accelerated a fundamental convergence of U.S. and Soviet strategic principles, the specific evidence most often cited in this regard is the ABM Treaty, whose preamble language and supporting provisions bar both sides from building nationwide defenses against ICBM attack. Soviet commitment to this ban— dramatically at variance with a long effort to achieve effective strategic defense of the Soviet homeland—has naturally been interpreted to mean that the Soviet side has finally seen the light and adopted the American doctrine of mutual assured destruction.

Although the ABM Treaty appears to open a significant chink in the edifice of traditional Soviet strategic thought and represents at least semantic convergence in the ABM field, it does not necessarily follow that the Soviets have come around to full-fledged embrace of the American strategic philosophy. The renunciation of countrywide ABM, for that matter, goes only part way toward acceptance of the mutual assured destruction concept.

The other key element is a delicate concern for the mutual survivability of offensive deterrent forces. Although the Soviets have for some time taken measures to improve the survivability of their own forces, as noted previously, they have not seemed disposed to eschew measures that threaten the opponent's forces, such as guidance improvements and deployment of counterforce systems. Conceptually, the Soviets have continued to reject the idea of security based on "the balance of terror," which is inherent in the doctrine of assured destruction.

IMPLICATIONS FOR FUTURE SOVIET POLICY

But if SALT to date has not proved to be the crucible in which important differences between Soviet and American strategic conceptions have been finally melted away, should this be taken to mean that future Soviet strategic policy will remain unaffected by the SALT experience? One can hardly make such a categorical assertion. Rather, there would seem to be room for at least two differing hypotheses as to the direction in which Soviet strategic policy may move under the impact of SALT and other developments affecting the Soviet-U.S. relationship.

The first hypothesis would tend to credit the ABM Treaty as a genuine conceptual departure from previous Soviet dedication to active defense, and as a real, even though not unequivocal, step away from traditional strategic thinking, which encouraged an endless search for comprehensive war-fighting and survival capabilities. In this view, the apparent continued adherence of the Soviet Union to strong air defense, to development of new missile systems with counterforce potential, and to a large civil defense effort may all merely reflect uneven erosion of the old doctrinal legacy. By the same token, it might be argued that institutionalized expression of a new rationale along the lines of assured destruction—and embodying explicit concern for the *mutual* survivability of offensive forces—simply has not had time to catch up.

Further, the point can be made that within the top Soviet leadership itself adherence to the perceived dictates of traditional strategic doctrine may prove more controversial now that "equality" has been achieved and the overriding consensus to overtake the United States has been satisfied. Given the political, ideological, and institutional disparities still existing between the two sides, this hypothesis, which might be labeled "creeping convergence by erosion," does not necessarily foresee a complete shift in the Soviet strategic outlook that would make it convergent in all respects with

American thinking. It does imply, however, that one can expect further significant Soviet movement in SALT and in future postural decisions toward the U.S. position on strategic issues of cardinal concern—foremost, mutual survivability of offensive forces.

By contrast, the second hypothesis would tend to raise doubt that the ABM Treaty marked a fundamental watershed in Soviet strategic policy, holding instead that it probably represents a practical compromise that still allows Soviet strategic theorists and planners to seek alternative ways of meeting the traditional premises of Soviet doctrine. In this view, the reversal of past Soviet positions on ABM, which made the ABM Treaty possible, was dictated in the main by concern over a superior U.S. Safeguard technology, and had little to do with agreement in principle that "the balance of terror"—holding populations hostage—should become the keystone of Soviet security. By a twist of reverse logic, indeed, it can be argued that the Soviets simply demonstrated the high value they still place on ABM, for in order to block U.S. development in this field, they were willing to accept constraints on their own.

Under this hypothesis, a deemphasis on the ABM aspect of strategic defense could have the effect of shifting the damage-limitation mission, traditionally close to the hearts of Soviet planners, in the further direction of counterforce systems. Even the ABM Treaty in this case might be construed as a useful means for enhancing the counterforce potential of Soviet strategic systems, insofar as it places strict limits on U.S. protection of ICBM launch sites and control centers.

Basically, this second hypothesis holds that the Soviets continue to be dominated primarily by concern for their own security and how to eliminate perceived or potential threats to it, rather than thinking about ensuring the security of their competitors as well. It might be inferred, therefore, that the Soviets would be prepared to take such steps as jettisoning the ABM Treaty, if technology permits and substantial new threats to their security seem to arise, as from China. At the least, this hypothesis implies that Soviet movement toward U.S. conceptions of strategic stability is no more likely than stubborn adherence to a strategic doctrine that preaches the importance of being able to knock out the forces of the opponent and to limit the damage that could be inflicted on one's own society.

Needless to say, which of these hypotheses about the future thrust of Soviet strategic policy comes closer to the mark is not something to be settled by essays on the subject like this one. The persuasive arguments will be those that emerge from further stages of SALT and from actual developments in the Soviet strategic posture itself. But to offer a prescriptive observation here, it would appear wise not to tie the prospects of a satisfactory adjustment of the U.S.-Soviet strategic relationship to the strategic convergence route. A better guideline would appear to be to aim at minimizing the damage to U.S. interests if optimistic assumptions about Soviet convergent tendencies go unfulfilled, and at not foreclosing the chance of tenable agreements if the Soviets prove less intractable than a pessimistic appraisal of their motivations might suggest.

Finally, it must be noted that there is an inherent blind spot in any discussion of the convergence issue couched—as this one has been—essentially in terms of the likelihood of a Soviet shift toward American strategic conceptions. This rather ethnocentric view of things implies that if any fundamental convergence is to take place, it will be a matter of the Soviet side coming to accept American tutelage in strategic matters. But a shift could also occur in the other direction. Thus, it is not to be ruled out that the interaction in SALT and elsewhere between the Soviet and American sides may eventually culminate in the movement of U.S. views closer to those held by the Soviets, rather than the reverse.

NOTE: The author wishes to acknowledge his indebtedness to a former colleague, Fritz Ermarth, for many of the points developed in this essay, although responsibility for its line of argument is the author's alone.

* The "knee" of the curve in question graphically depicts the point at which delivery of additional nuclear weapons ceases to

result in any substantial increase in fatalities. The flattening of the curve beyond this point also can be said to reflect what is popularly described as "overkill."

ABOUT THE AUTHOR: Soviet specialist Thomas Wolfe (Ph.D., Georgetown) began his career as a journalist and foreign correspondent. During a 20-year career with the Air Force, he served as intelligence officer, staff officer in the Joint Chiefs of Staff, and air attaché at the U.S. Embassy in Moscow. In 1960 he was made a delegate to the Ten-Nation Disarmament Conference in Geneva and Director of the Sino-Soviet Affairs Division in the Office of the Secretary of Defense. Since he joined Rand in 1962, Dr. Wolfe has authored several major works on Soviet military and foreign policy. He is a member of the National Security Research Center in Washington.

For many, if not most, large social problems, no one really knows what to do.

Garry D. Brewer

Experimentation and the Policy Process

It is now common to point out how complex and how difficult to resolve are the many problems which beset our society. The problems are not new, but they seem more pervasive, and at least we now know that we can and must do something about them. Unfortunately, we have undertaken measures to alleviate some problems only to find that we did not like the consequences and have failed to achieve our objectives.

However, while we can point to unexpected and unintended effects of tinkering with social problems, there is an urgent sense that much more must be done to invent new and better policies.

How can policymakers institute needed change in a complex society without exacting exorbitant costs or inducing extraordinary disruptions? How can they find out in advance that a program may not work as intended, and avoid wasting scarce resources?

By carrying out carefully designed small-scale social experiments, social scientists hope to gather enough reliable information on the complex effects of a proposed program to allow decisionmakers to make better-informed choices among possible programs before they decide upon full-scale implementation.

Although social experimentation has roots in the methods of the natural sciences, a social experiment differs fundamentally from either a "clean" natural science experiment, containing carefully selected and measurable variables whose interrelationships are known with some accuracy, or even a "not so clean" psychological experiment, also containing a few measurable variables whose interrelationships are the object of study.

Social experiments confront problems and have objectives that differ substantially from those of natural science experiments. Experimentation in the social setting involves the systematic comparison of policy objectives and strategies in terms of their causes and effects, as well as this can be determined; of the consideration of variables, some measurable and others not; of goals held by relevant participants; and of the institutional practices in which these objectives, strategies, and goals are embedded.

In practice, a social experiment is an organized attempt to pretest a particular innovative policy before committing vast resources to the solution of some large social problem. An example might be the experiment in New Jersey with income maintenance, undertaken before there was a national commitment to such a program. In this case, alternative programs were tested on sample populations in several other states. The same approach characterizes the experiment with housing allowances. In this instance there will be parallel tests to assess the supply response to housing allowances, a demand experiment, and tests of alternative administrative structures. In yet another context, educational vouchers are being used to assess how parents and pupils respond to alternative programs being offered in the public schools in the Alum Rock district of San Jose, California.

WHY EXPERIMENT?

There are many reasons for conducting social experiments: scientific reasons, to enhance our understanding of the world and society; normative and ethical reasons, to assess alternatives from several human and humane perspectives; technical reasons, relating to the relative importance of policies, the time constraints associated with alternative policies, and the relative costs of various options; efficiency reasons, because large-scale social programs are costly and may be irreversible; and finally, political reasons, arising from an operator's need to propose a chosen policy with as little uncertainty about probable outcomes as possible.

Perhaps the purest answer to the question "Why experiment?" is tied intimately to the quest for knowledge itself. Because intervention in our social system now depends to a large degree on guesswork, expediency, and compromise, any procedure that allows consideration of a wider-ranging and more objective assessment of policy alternatives should be examined carefully. Experimentation is one such procedure.

A major strength of the technique is that it reveals empirical information about various social objectives. The tradeoffs among competing objectives and between various recipient groups are subjected to partial experience—an important intermediate step between speculation and full-scale implementation.

There are several technical reasons for conducting social experiments. For large and complex systems, it is often useful to identify relationships and constraints that are sensitive to small changes. These elements may be the key to the behavior of the overall system. Because small changes may have unexpectedly large consequences, and because no one can foresee all important interactions and outcomes, it is necessary to experiment on a carefully defined and limited basis to determine the likely outcomes of a variety of planned interventions.

A valid experimental design is crucial. Because an experiment by definition is conducted in some less-than-total setting, extraneous and diversionary features of the environment should be minimized. This requires pre-experimental analysis and modeling to formalize one's views about the environment, to suggest where experimental changes might have the greatest impacts, and to serve as a "blueprint" to be revised as the experiment is carried out and as new, detailed information is obtained.

Concern for social efficiency underlies many efforts to experiment. Tests, limited in scope and controlled with a solid experimental design, are a far less expensive way to examine plausible interventions than is the blind commitment of major resources. Not only do experiments cost less in absolute dollar terms, but for a given number of dollars many more options may be measured, tested, and compared. There is really no reason to be satisfied with only one or two large and possibly "irreversible" policy options. Not only is the one-option strategy unsatisfactory, but there are good reasons to be wary of any one or two "answers" that have not been subjected to partial testing and assessment.

As small children we all experienced the comforting feeling that mother or father (or some grown-up) really knew what to do in a trying situation; someone, somewhere, "knew" and would take care of us. For many, if not most, large social problems, *no one really knows what to do.* No one really "knows"; no one really understands many of the incredibly complex systems in which we all routinely participate; and no one really knows how to make them work better, more efficiently, or more equitably. We must face these facts, and social experimentation is addressed directly to this hard process, for better or worse.

Many of these concerns turn out to be largely political issues. A well-executed experiment may provide more and better information about real options so that the politician may perform better—selecting from among a wide range of options the one or the few most likely to accomplish society's objectives. Furthermore, consensus building is enhanced if information about a number of plausible alternatives and associated outcomes is laid out for public consideration.

WHY NOT EXPERIMENT?

There are also reasons why social experimentation should *not* be carried out; the method is not a panacea. These counterarguments include scientific, ethical, methodological, institutional, and political dimensions that must be taken seriously.

Scientific Reasons

A purist might argue that the social experiment prematurely closes off options from consideration by the simple expedient of having to identify a set of alternatives before the experiment is carried out. Such selection may prevent new ideas, determined as the experiment progresses or as knowledge about the problem improves, from being examined and possibly chosen for implementation.

Because an experiment is a limited and controlled procedure, there will always be some doubt about the validity of transferring and generalizing the experience to larger populations and to less-controlled settings. This may be a sufficient reason not to trust an experimental result without conducting additional investigations to determine the effects of a selected option in a less-controlled setting.

Ethical Reasons

The ethical and human dimensions of social experiments have seldom received the attention they warrant. Whose preferences are being represented in the various options proposed for experimental testing? How are those options determined, measured, and specifically related to individuals? How are different benefits received by experimental subjects reconciled and justified? At the conclusion of an experiment, how does one make restitution for an experimental alternative not finally chosen but upon which recipients have become dependent? What about confidentiality of data and other human problems associated with the conduct of the experiment? These and many other primarily ethical issues all come into play and must be accounted for by the social experimenter.

Methodological Reasons

An assortment of methodological problems confront the social experimenter. A persistent one is to translate into operational terms the goals held by various participants so that comparable tradeoff calculations may be carried out. It is not a trivial problem to define and then measure some criterion or other, but it is a fundamental requirement of the experimental technique.

Social measurement has not progressed so far that one can, with confidence, reach into a tool kit for pretested, much-used, and reliable measures of experimental outcomes. In fact, much ingenuity is needed to develop and test measures of experimental results. Not only is the general issue of measurement validity a thorny problem, but one is continually confronted with the specific task of reconciling the ongoing experiment with the setting in which it is carried out. Are the measurements valid, accurate, and reliable? And if they are not, what can be done about it?

It would be helpful if there were well-developed and reliable social indicators to reduce the measurement problem. The need to devise multiple measures of experimental outcomes (social events are not unidimensional) may result in the proposing and testing of a variety of possible indicators in the course of one or two large social experiments.

Institutional Reasons

Institutional problems are many, and run the gamut from difficulties in choosing experimental sites to the composition of the group conducting the experiment. Ideally, experimental sites should in significant ways mirror the larger setting in which the results will be implemented.

What constitutes "significant ways" is the basic problem. Should one pick a single location that in demographic, socioeconomic, and political characteristics is a microcosm of the larger setting? Or, should sites be selected to reveal the impacts of the experimental alternatives when administered by various institutional structures, each having rather different political and administrative capabilities? Arguments for the second strategy concentrate on the not-well-understood but critical issue of policy implementation. Or, should one select sites having vastly different sociological characteristics? Arguments for this strategy stress the need to anticipate the nonobvious impacts of interventions. No one of these strategies is "correct" or "best," and the ultimate choice often turns out to be a judgmental or negotiated matter of some consequence.

We have already alluded to the possibility that the experimental design may close off options by the choice of alternatives to be considered. Does one compromise "scientific" standards by adjusting the experiment in midcourse as a result of information generated in the experimental design? Clearly, one must try to maintain scientific standards; however, there is no certainty that the set of alternatives initially selected is the best or most complete. Should *sequential design* be considered? One form of experiment allows the researcher to choose a final design as more information becomes available, a choice that might be considered if there are limits on the size of field operations that can be undertaken. On these issues there may be continuing disagreement between experimental purists and more action-oriented and pragmatic operators. Because there is no clear way around the problem, recognition of its existence may at least temper acrimonious mutual recriminations.

A third institutional problem centers on the composition of the group conducting the experiment. It is nearly axiomatic that the group will be multidisciplinary, since no individual or any group from a single discipline is likely to be able to carry out the experiment alone. There is an additional, complicating problem. The experimental group needs to have access to the operational setting, but at the same time must resist being distracted by day-to-day operational problems. How does one keep in intimate contact with a real setting without being captured by those actually operating in that setting? How does one safeguard against an eager operator's desire to take one of the partially tested experimental options and to implement it prematurely? Again, there are no easy answers.

Political Reasons

An experiment may only be a substitute for much needed action. Difficult or politically sensitive problems are often referred to an expert commission for advice and recommendations. This may merely drag out the final resolution and buy time for a politician who may not be around when the commission files its report and recommendations. Experiments could also be used as a political stalling tactic; they are usually hard to carry out and require considerable time to design and execute properly. If an experiment is primarily a substitute for action, then one might legitimately decide not to experiment at all.

Implementation is also a problem. Bureaucracies are not equally endowed with competent people. The clean and relatively unambiguous results obtained under experimental conditions may fail to materialize when implemented by less capable or by differently motivated bureaucrats. Furthermore, an experiment may promise results beyond the capacity of the average or less capable bureaucracies to deliver. When an experimental option is badly or improperly implemented, the harm done in terms of lost confidence and popular disillusionment may far exceed any possible benefits.

An experiment may raise expectations to the point where it is clearly and practically infeasible to satisfy them. For instance, tested options may turn out to be so expensive, even though effective, that no right-minded politician would be able to endorse any of them. However, if the experiment has been carried out, there is likely to be some demand for its wider application. All alternatives may be infeasible, even obviously so, before the experiment is undertaken. In such a case, it may be sensible not to experiment at all.

A politician may elect not to experiment to avoid being associated with some unconventional or controversial options that are legitimately incorporated in the experimental design. There are alternatives. The researchers may determine what the politician fears and modify the design accordingly. Or, the experiment may be conducted without the formal or tacit approval of the responsible politician. Each of these accommodations has costs, and if the costs are judged to be excessive, this may be sufficient reason to cancel the planned experiment or to address the fundamental problem in other ways.

Other reasons why an experiment may not be carried out include the fact that some problems are trivial or of limited scope: experiments are costly and nonexperimental research may do the job better. And experiments should not be relied on when the pressure for quick solutions is great, as in the case of a crisis situation. Good experiments take time to execute.

Several general classes of problems confronting a would-be social experimenter have been stressed. That no easy answers have been offered should not be taken as a reason *not* to experiment. Quite the contrary, experimentation has considerable promise as a policy-assisting method, but, as with many things in social life, there are no "pat" answers, only plenty of worrisome issues that must be dealt with as forthrightly as possible.

SOCIAL EXPERIMENTS AND THE POLICY PROCESS

To locate social experimentation in the general policymaking process is to call attention, in yet another way, to several of the possible benefits and many of the real limitations of the technique.

For convenience a public policy or program may be imagined as having a "life," a sequence of events through which it flows from earliest initiation to its eventual termination. This process is first described and then experimentation is related to it.

The Policy Process

Invention or initiation, the earliest phase of the policy process, begins when a problem is first sensed. At this point, a number of ways to alleviate it may be proposed, including many ill-defined and inappropriate "solutions." This phase, marked by a casting about for answers, should help to sharpen and redefine the problem.

Estimation, the second logical step in the process, deals with risks, costs, and benefits associated with each candidate solution suggested in the invention phase. Estimation implies narrowing the range of plausible solutions (by excluding the infeasible or the truly exploitative, for instance) and ordering the remaining options according to scientific *and* evaluative criteria. A battery of sophisticated methodologies is available for this purpose. Social experiments represent an interesting combination of scientific and evaluative perspectives, a point to which we return shortly.

The third, or selection, phase is most easily seen as the "political" step. Someone, usually the policymaker, must select from the "invented" and "estimated" options. The policymaker must strike a balance between the analyst's rational calculations and the multiple, changing, and conflicting goals held by society at large.

Implementation refers to the execution of the selected option. As evidenced by a heightened interest in and statements of concern about the failures of policy implementation, this is a phase of the overall policy process that is little understood, not particularly appreciated, and not well developed. We need to think more systematically about implementation and to integrate it into the other phases of the policy process. Certainly one must understand implementation mechanisms before government performance can be evaluated and improved, the next step in the sequence.

Initiation or invention and estimation are primarily forward-looking activities. Selection stresses the urgency of the present. Evaluation is basically backward-looking, concerned with inquiries about system performance and individual responsibility. Typical topics and questions reflected in the idea of evaluation include the following: What officials and what policies and programs were successful or unsuccessful? How can one assess and measure performance? What criteria were used to make those measurements? Who made the assessment, and what were the assessor's purposes? Evaluation is a necessary input to the next and final phase of the sequence.

Termination or adjustment is necessary when policies and programs have become dysfunctional, redundant, outmoded, unnecessary, and so forth. From the conceptual point of view, it is not a well-developed phase; however, one should not underrate its importance. How, for instance, can a policy be adjusted or terminated without having been thoroughly evaluated? Who suffers from the termination? What provisions for redress have to be considered? What personal costs are involved by termination? Can they be met? What can be learned from termination that will inform the initiation and invention of new policies or programs in the same or related fields? The list of relevant questions is long, but neither these questions nor the fact that termination is linked intimately to other steps in the policy process should be ignored.

How does experimentation fit into the phases of this rather abbreviated and stylized characterization of the policy process?

Experimentation and Policymaking

In the initiation or invention phase, prototyping will allow systematic but relatively unstructured efforts to generate a full range of options for subsequent consideration. So conceived, prototyping is a precondition to full-scale experimentation. It is exploratory, and seeks to assess new options in the light of existing institutional practices.

For example, rather than conjecturing about various proposals to construct large-scale community information utilities, it may be a more efficient and effective strategy to develop a limited prototype utility to determine political-institutional, technical, and administrative-managerial effects. A basic feature of the prototype, as distinguished from the social experiment, is that the policy alternatives considered are at best imperfectly and incompletely known. By constructing a prototype, one may reach an initial agreement on a testable set of experimental options.

Systematic experimentation is well suited to the estimation phase of the policy process where several alternatives may be simultaneously tested according to both scientific and evaluative criteria; however, one needs to make some important conceptual distinctions between *natural experiments, random innovations,* and more *systematic forms of experimentation.* A common feature of these experimental forms is that novel options have been tested or partially realized in some limited setting. A common deficiency of current policy practice is that these experiences are seldom carefully evaluated and information about them is not made generally available. As a result, the wheel gets reinvented with distressing regularity.

For example, management information system development has progressed in the "natural" way in a number of municipalities over the past decade. However, no thorough evaluation of those natural experiments has been carried out. In effect, a large but uncoordinated and unevaluated investment in natural experiments has been made, but lacking a systematic experimental orientation, general social dividends from it have not yet been realized. Many of these natural social experiments exist, but we have not yet capitalized on the general lessons they provide about political, technical, and administrative opportunities and problems.

Random innovations could also be integrated better into the policy process, and adopting a general experimental attitude might be one way to do it. There is a biological revolution of dramatic proportions confronting mankind, a revolution characterized by random alterations of the genetic basis of life itself. However, this random experimentation is not accompanied by any systematic or careful investigation of the implications it may have for us all. What human and institutional measures must be developed to control these random events in ways congenial to the full development of man? We have scarcely even begun to recognize the problem, much less turn our full attention to its resolution.

If an experiment has been carried out well, it should contribute to the final choice of one of the tested alternatives. Hopefully, more and better information will have been generated in the course of the experiment, information that cannot easily be ignored and that will in significant ways improve and focus debate about issues involved in the choice.

Implementation may be enhanced by conducting social experiments. First of all, the experiment may provide vital clues about the operation of institutional and individual incentive systems vis-à-vis a set of tested alternatives. Because implementation seems to depend delicately on such incentive systems, the experiment affords a preview of how equally plausible options will be treated. That, in itself, may be sufficient reason to experiment. Finally, eventual implementation may be speeded because the alternative chosen will have been operationally tested; participants will "know" how to get a new but partly tested program under way.

The connection between implementation, evaluation, and social experimentation has been mentioned. An experiment may yield a variety of valuable performance indicators. For instance, how much should an option cost for a given amount of service or output delivered; how long should a given procedure take to implement; and how many persons are needed to carry out detailed tests of the option? Such performance measures serve as initial evaluation criteria for the option's more general implementation. Rigid adherence to experimentally derived measures is not expected, but such measures provide a point of departure for detailed follow-up.

Possible impacts of the social experiment on the termination phase of the sequence are not predictable, primarily because we have not yet had adequate experience. In principle, the experiment should begin to shed light on whether the studied problem is going to be chronic, recurring, or resolvable. If chronic, one would expect slight demand for termination (as is the case of Medicare or Social Security); if recurring, one might consider building into the selected option termination provisions that are a function of service demand (as is the case with disaster relief programs); and if the problem appears to be resolvable, termination provisions might be built in directly (as was the case with polio prevention research).

By relating social experimentation to the policy process, some of the possible benefits inherent in the technique are revealed. Figure 1 shows how various benefits may emerge from each

Phase in the Policy Process	Possible Benefits
Initiation/Invention	• Creative thinking about a problem • Prototypical design • Crude hypothesis testing • Preliminary investigation of concepts or claims
Estimation	• Scientific examination of likely impacts and outcomes of a set of plausible options • Normative/evaluative examination of likely human impacts of plausible options • Development of outlines of a complex program • Thorough evaluation of concepts or claims • Establishment of a first approximation of performance indicators • Detailed estimation of critical parameters
Selection	• Focusing debate on the actual issues • Allowance for "cleaner," less "hedged," or "compromised" options to be selected • Choice among program designs • Reduction of uncertainty about various options
Implementation	• Development of specific, difficult pieces of a program • Development of a complex program giving due respect to existing institutional and incentive structures • Minimization of implementation costs • Establishment of performance expectations based on estimates of critical parameters for selected option • Reduction in unexpected and unwanted "surprises" from program implementation
Evaluation	• Comparison of estimated performance levels with those actually attained • Reconciliation of expected institutional responses with those actually observed
Termination	• Predetermination of whether the problem is chronic, recurring, or resolvable • Generation of information about new problems, some of which may require experimental treatment

Fig. 1. Possible benefits from each phase of the policy process.

phase of the policy process. The list is impressive. However, the promises of social experimentation are still far from being realized and there are many pitfalls along the way. Realizing the potential is an intricate and formidable challenge, but the rewards for meeting the challenge squarely seem well worth the considerable difficulties involved.

ABOUT THE AUTHOR: *As a doctoral student in political science at Yale, Garry Brewer did research for the Defense Advanced Research Projects Agency and was a consultant to Rand. In 1970/1971 he took a professorship at Berkeley, followed by a lecture series at the University of California at Los Angeles and the University of Southern California. On the permanent Rand staff since then, and on the faculty of the Rand Graduate Institute for Policy Studies, Dr. Brewer has worked on the theory and techniques of operational gaming, developing criteria for validating, evaluating, and costing games. His other research interests include the appraisal of policies and programs for handicapped children, and the design and implementation of regional information systems in several national settings.*

... in the balance of power between a citizen and the totality of systems that keep records about him, he is at a significant disadvantage.

551-50-1566

Willis H. Ware

Data Banks, Privacy, and Society

Computer technology provides society with the tool it needs to accommodate growing information requirements. It lets us keep the records we have to keep, economically and efficiently. But the computer-based automated file can also work against us. The information in computer systems can be valuable and thus subverted for inappropriate purposes. Because of this vulnerability, automated data systems add a new dimension to the problem of personal privacy, as well as provide opportunity for embezzlement, blackmail, and other fraudulent schemes. Our essential tool could become a major societal threat unless we provide effective safeguards to protect personal information in automated files and those to whom it pertains.

The attitude of the public with regard to personal information has changed in recent years. We are becoming increasingly aware of data files and the information they contain about us.

To some data systems we provide personal information voluntarily. We do this in exchange for some benefit, privilege, or opportunity: we want to make credit-card purchases, obtain loans, write checks, get a passport, apply for a job. Some information we provide because it is required by law: we participate in the census or fill out questionnaires for military service. Sometimes we provide information inadvertently: we are in an accident that involves a police record.

We provide considerable information because we ask for services from government. We want educational assistance, unemployment support, housing allowance, or care for the older segment of the population. Congress, in turn, insists on strict accountability of public assistance programs and on evaluation of the success of such undertakings; this requires personal records and computer processing. The more extensively we and the government interact, the more extensive must be the records that need to be compiled and maintained by computer.

INFORMATION NEEDS OF GOVERNMENT

As our population increases and our society becomes more complex, and as the government enlarges its range of services, the need for personal information grows. The federal government, for example, needs extensive information in order to formulate new legislation, to adopt sound fiscal and tax policies, for entitlement decisions with regard to public assistance programs, to estimate the consequences of a possible decision, and to generally conduct the affairs of the country.

In the face of increased demand for natural resources—and many man-made resources—comprehensive planning becomes crucial at all levels of government. To adequately balance quantity and demand for land, energy, water, highways, etc., government regulation and intervention are required. Local governments need information to regulate land use, and to plan sewage and water facilities, transportation, and many other public services.

Industry gathers much personal information in order to assemble and maintain the records that are required in an era of intricate labor relations, widespread union practices, pension and insurance plans, state and federal tax withholding, and other regulatory and legal restrictions. Social research is also increasing, and along with it social experimentation, so that more information about people, their behavior, and their habits must be gathered. Thus, there exist numerous automated files containing extensive personal information about all of us.

ACCESSIBILITY OF PERSONAL INFORMATION

For whatever reason we furnish information about ourselves, we implicitly tend to assume that it will be used only in our best interest and solely for the purpose for which it is furnished. Thus it comes as a surprise when we find that the information we have provided for one purpose is being used for a different one. As a result of personal data submitted for a driving license, for example, we find ourselves on a mailing list and inundated with advertising literature.

While much personal information in automated files is anonymous, describing in a statistical way some characteristic segment of the population, there is also much that is identifiable in order to permit decisions to be made based on a person's record. Given our mobility in residence and employment, many organizations find it expedient to exchange data or to transport information about an individual from one place to another. Thus the automated record system tends to concentrate information about people in one place and to provide ready accessibility to it for a wide group of users. Moreover, automated systems can, in principle, exchange data automatically with one another and so broaden the exposure of personal information. Such linking of files, when it occurs, enlarges the volume of data available to any one inquirer.

Of the many files containing personal, private information, a
considerable number are at government level: census data,
social security records, Internal Revenue Service tax records,
various research collections in the social and life sciences, etc.
Some are in the financial industry: bank account records,
savings and loan records, stock investment records, credit
records. Many relate to health care, such as hospital, medical,
or psychiatric records. A few have been collected by the
recreational and leisure-time industry in the course of making
reservations and travel plans. Those accumulated by
educational institutions include a complete, detailed account of
performance in high school and college.

SOCIAL SECURITY NUMBERS AS IDENTIFIERS

If the file is for a local purpose, it may be sufficient to identify
the individual by his name and address. Often some secondary
identification is included; the mother's maiden name is one
traditional example. In many instances, federal statutes
require that a person's social security number be given as an
authenticator of his identity; financial institutions, for
instance, are legally required to obtain it.

Federal statutes or regulations will, in some cases, authorize
the exchange of information among data banks. The Internal
Revenue Service, for example, regularly exchanges data with
state tax-collection agencies; and in so doing, ensures that
identity is preserved and records are kept straight by means of
the social security number. In other cases, an administrative
action will stipulate that social security numbers must be
obtained. They are required by the Department of Motor
Vehicles in some states, for example. Occasionally, social
security numbers are secured for no particular purpose other
than as a hedge against an unknown future need. Some
educational organizations use them as student identifiers.

Unfortunately, the growing number of automated files in
which a record about an individual includes his social security
number implicitly encourages the exchange of information; it
also serves as a key for combining information from several
sources. Sometimes, exchange of data is facilitated by
freedom-of-information acts at both federal and state levels,

because these acts require that public information be provided to any requester. A person who finds himself in a file considered to be public information has no effective control over how his information will be used.

While linkage among information systems is undoubtedly not yet so widespread as to be considered at the critical level, many factors suggest that the situation is likely to develop: the remote-access computer systems that service geographically distributed users; the awareness by a manager or an official that information from some other sources will help him do his job better; recognition by a researcher that combinations of files will give him more insight into his problems; and the economic efficiency of combining several small information systems into a large one serving many classes of users.

CONTROL OF PERSONAL RECORDS

With this growing awareness that automated files pose a real threat to personal privacy, we are becoming more sensitive to the misuse of personal information, and are willing to complain about it. Our complaint may simply be the result of a personal annoyance—a dunning letter received because a paid bill has not been accurately posted to the correct account; but the complaint can be much more serious. Because of incomplete or erroneous information in an automated file, we may suffer a damaged reputation, loss of financial status or position in the community, the denial of credit, the loss of a job, or improper arrest.

Public concern over the invasion of personal privacy may well rest more on a sense of having lost control—of not knowing when information freely given for one purpose will be used for another—than on the feeling of being surrounded by a data-hungry environment. We feel a need to be guaranteed that personal, identifiable records will be used in ways over which we have some control—and that we have a mechanism to seek recourse in case we should sustain harm if they are improperly used.

The Constitution of the United States does not *specifically* provide for a right of personal privacy. Justice Brandeis, dissenting in the case of *Olmstead* v. *the United States* (1928), first suggested that personal privacy is implied in the Constitution. A continuing series of judicial interpretations have cumulatively created the right of privacy. The legal basis for these judgments includes the first amendment guarantee of free speech, press, assembly, and religion; the third amendment prohibition against quartering soldiers in private homes; the fourth amendment right to security from unreasonable search and seizure; the fifth amendment right against compulsory self-incrimination; and the ninth amendment guarantee of other unenumerated rights retained by the people.

Recent Supreme Court decisions have declared the right of personal privacy as the basis for protecting such freedoms of an individual as the practice of contraception or the reading of pornography in the home. Unlike the United States, other countries—Canada, for example—have not developed a constitutional or legal basis for extending personal privacy to its citizens.

From the standpoint of the individual citizen, he is generally unaware that information about himself is being disseminated without his approval; in most instances he is powerless to stop it even if he should discover it. Since large information systems are a relatively recent development in a technical and operational sense, one can expect to find inadequacies in their designs or incomplete operational practices, either of which can be manipulated to steal information, or can result in inadvertent or malicious leakage of information to someone not authorized to have it. Furthermore, information in data banks is usually not protected against legal process. While specific legislation does sometimes protect information in automated files, or authorizes a government official to extend protection as he sees fit, by and large, the bulk of information in such files is subject to confiscation through administrative or legal subpoena or through other court-directed seizure.

HOW TO ACHIEVE PROPER BALANCE?

Thus the exploitation of computer and communication technology in modern recordkeeping systems highlights the central confrontation between the need of government and business organizations to have personal information for efficient planning and operation and the need of the individual to have control over the way in which information about himself is used. How can we achieve a more satisfactory balance?

There are actually two quite different issues involved. One is the technical problem of designing and implementing an automated information system that will safeguard the data it contains. A properly designed system will not inadvertently leak information, and it will be physically protected against pilfering, thievery, and infiltration. It will deliver information only to users authorized to have it.

The other issue is the much more difficult one of controlling what personal information should be collected in the first place, of determining who shall have access to it and for what purpose, and of giving the individual more control over information about himself. Unlike the control exercised over national security information, there is no classification scheme established by law or executive order for labeling personal information as "sensitive," "nonsensitive," or "ultrasensitive"; nor are there any government-wide guidelines for establishing who may have access to it. Thus, the rules and regulations governing dissemination of personal information from a file tend to be made by the individual or organization that collects the data and owns the file. In many instances, there are no established practices to serve as a model for good procedure. In the particular case of consumer credit reference systems, the Fair Credit Reporting Act does impose limited constraints; for example, provision is made for the individual to inspect his file and to correct it.

SOME SUGGESTIONS FOR SOLVING THE PROBLEM

In solving the technical problem, physical protection, computer hardware and software safeguards, communication security safeguards, and a general management-procedural overlay are collectively necessary to provide the overall protection needed. In all of these areas, the requirement of the defense community to protect classified information is a driving force for research, new system designs, and general progress toward an eventual solution. Fortunately, many of these same safeguards are needed in any computer system that shares its resources among many users—that is, the time-shared computer system—and to this end the general advance of the computer industry will help to provide the technical basis needed.

In solving the problem of restricting the collection of personal information, of controlling its dissemination, of carefully specifying what use may be made of it, and of affording the individual greater participation in the dissemination of his personal information, various suggestions have been made but none have been generally implemented. To improve the care with which recordkeeping systems are designed and operated, one proposal is to certify computer programmers and system designers. This action would assuredly be a useful one; but unlike the older engineering fields, the computer field does not yet have a well-established body of preferred practice upon which to draw. Thus, while certification would be a helpful step, it would put the responsibility for a properly designed and controlled record system in the wrong place. The responsibility should be assumed by the organization that assembles the system, initiates its design, and operates it, not by the technician who implements it. While certification is a step in the right direction, it cannot of itself adequately solve the problem.

A second solution might be the ombudsman approach, which has been used for many years in Scandinavian countries. Basically, the ombudsman is a spokesman for an individual who has been harmed; he serves essentially as a communication channel between the person and the bureaucracy in matters of dispute. While the ombudsman concept is a useful third-party mechanism to facilitate resolution of argument, it is not a well-established mechanism in the United States nor can it function as a sufficiently strong force to be a solution for the entire problem of protecting personal privacy.

A third solution, one that attempts to deal with the problem through the established institutions and procedures of the country, would be to create by law a Code of Fair Information

Practices in the spirit of already existing legislation on labor practices. The intent of such a code would be to encourage ethical practice on the part of owners, designers, and operators of recordkeeping systems through legal deterrents. In this way it would be possible to specify how record systems should be organized and operated, how owners and operators should conduct their operations relative to the individuals about whom the information is held, what privileges and recourses the individual has, and to provide legal sanctions, both civil and criminal, that can be imposed for violations of the code.

The approach would have several advantages: It would exploit existing legal and judicial institutions and procedures. It would provide a self-adapting solution to the problem through the medium of court interpretation and judgment. It would require a minimum of new bureaucratic functions. With regard to industry, the code would be handled by the General Counsel's office, as are fair labor practices, tax matters, and other industrial regulations.

Finally, a fourth possibility is to create a Federal Record System Commission, similar to the Federal Communications Commission or the Civil Aeronautics Board, that would serve as a regulatory body to license, register, and oversee the operation of all record systems dealing with personal information. However, this would entail the creation of substantial new bureaucratic structure and funding for it. More importantly, it would also be another instance of government intervention in the affairs of the people and industry. Given our national aversion to government intervention in business and industrial activities, and the fact that deterrent mechanisms have not yet been tried, a regulatory approach to the problem of recordkeeping appears to be one that should be kept in abeyance until other methods have failed and the need for it is clearly established.

A NUMBERED SOCIETY?

The Social Security Amendments Act of 1972 (P.L. 92-603) is suggestive of what can happen if no action is taken. The Act requires that a social security number be issued to all individuals, of any age, who are receiving public assistance from federal funds. It also authorizes, but does not require, the Secretary of Health, Education, and Welfare to take affirmative measures to assign social security numbers to all children on their initial entrance into school.

Should future legislative trend follow this precedent and gradually require all sectors of the population to have a social security number, then the United States will have reached the stage at which the population is fully numbered, a national population register can exist, and it will be technically feasible to maintain a lifetime dossier on each citizen. Other forces can lead to the same end. The introduction of the national birth certificate number will, for example, provide a unique lifetime identification for each citizen.

While a fully numbered population may not of itself be undesirable, the alarming fact is that we are drifting toward this state without public awareness that it is happening or public debate as to the possible consequences. The end result—that each of us will have a unique and permanent identifier—is not likely to happen from a well-engineered plan or deliberate intent. Rather, it will be the combined effect of many decisions, each made by someone doing his best job as he sees it at the time. It will be the cumulative effect of a variety of legislative steps, some unnoticed data collections, and a gradual widening of the operational scope of existing record systems due to economic pressures, coupled with a general ignorance that such events are occurring. In sum, a United States citizen could easily awaken one morning to find that he is uniquely identified for life and that all sorts of personal information are being collected under his label and widely disseminated for public and private use.

A NEED FOR ACTION

The issue of personal privacy has several major public-action aspects. It must be brought before the public, and kept there; the active support of consumer-oriented organizations must be solicited to promote legislative measures; public participation in the debate about a fully numbered, registered society must be encouraged.

There are also researchable aspects. One is to examine the technical details of providing comprehensive safeguards for automated information systems. Another is to analyze the legal considerations involved in protecting the individual's right to privacy. Others are a study of the consequences of a fully numbered and registered society, a search for ways to provide comprehensive protection against abuse of personal information, and the development of means for linking automated data systems while protecting the personal privacy of the data subjects.

Since automated information systems containing personal information are essential to today's complex society, it is imperative that solutions be found to the important problem of protecting our inherent right to privacy. There is certainly no question but that in the balance of power between a citizen and the totality of systems that keep records about him, he is at a significant disadvantage.

ABOUT THE AUTHOR: In the late 1940s Willis Ware was doing research under John von Neumann on an electronic digital computer—the first of the "Princeton-class" machines. After receiving his doctorate from Princeton in electrical engineering, Dr. Ware came to Rand in 1952 to work on the exploitation of computers for military, scientific, and civil problems. He headed Rand's Computer Sciences Department from 1964 to 1971, and is at present on the Corporate Research Staff. Among his many advisory appointments, he is chairman of the Air Force Scientific Advisory Board's Information Processing Panel and of the Secretary's (DHEW) Advisory Committee on Automated Personal Data Systems.

Programs

In this section we provide survey descriptions of Rand's current research in three major program areas, each headed by a Rand vice president: Air Force Project RAND, under George K. Tanham; national security research for the Office of the Secretary of Defense, and other agencies, under John P. White; and domestic research, under Gustave H. Shubert.

In addition, we include short descriptions of The New York City–Rand Institute—about which much more information is provided in its own annual report, published earlier this year—and of the Rand Graduate Institute for Policy Studies.

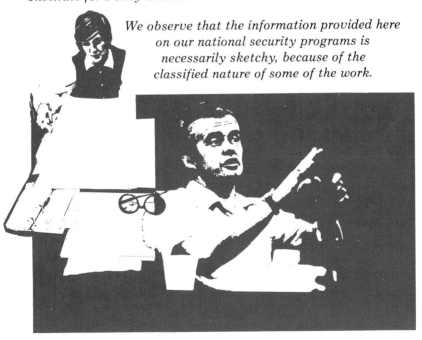

We observe that the information provided here on our national security programs is necessarily sketchy, because of the classified nature of some of the work.

NATIONAL SECURITY RESEARCH: PROJECT RAND

Project RAND—our work for the U.S. Air Force—represents about one-third of Rand's total research effort. The work is divided into a number of research areas, or programs, which are in turn divided into projects staffed by one to perhaps half-a-dozen researchers of different skills, the number depending on the scope, complexity, and urgency of the work.

The makeup of programs and the projects within them varies from time to time, with the emphasis shifting according to Air Force and Rand perceptions of need. Program composition is thus jointly determined, with Rand and the Air Force having more or less an equal say in the matter, and initiatives as likely to come from one as the other.

The mechanism for this is the Project RAND Air Force Advisory Group, which is both our formal link to the Air Force leadership and the overseer of all Project RAND work. The group consists of general officers of the Air Staff—currently eight—who meet formally at least once a year and more often informally as needed. Rand communicates with the Air Force not only through the Advisory Group, but also through direct, frequent, and informal contacts between Rand staff members and officials of the Air Force at all levels.

At present, Project RAND consists of six research programs: Strategic Studies; General-Purpose Forces; Logistics; R&D and Acquisition; Manpower, Personnel, and Training; and Supporting Research. We discuss each of them briefly below.

Strategic Studies

Current trends are raising serious questions about the long-term future of nuclear deterrence and the roles of strategic forces, especially those that support U.S. alliance commitments and foreign policy. In the Strategic Arms Limitation Talks, for example, the United States is seeking agreements that will limit these forces both quantitatively and qualitatively. Budget pressures may lead to unilateral reductions as well. Moreover, the willingness of the United States and its allies to maintain adequate conventional forces seems to be decreasing, while Soviet and Chinese military power and nth-country nuclear proliferation possibilities are increasing.

Research in the strategic studies program is focusing on the long-term implications of these issues for Air Force strategic systems and for U.S. strategic policy. We are also examining a number of contextual factors that influence choices and priorities among objectives, strategies, criteria, and forces. These include Soviet and Chinese nuclear doctrine, arms limitation agreements and negotiations, weapons system cost and strategic force budgets, and new technology.

General-Purpose Forces

During most of 1972 this program (formerly titled "Tactical Studies Program") continued to center on problems of tactical resource allocation and force structure. The major new study in the redirected program will look at the implications of precision guided weapons systems for future operations of surface vessels, armored forces, tactical nuclear weapons, airbases, and delivering airpower. Our examination of European security issues includes an analysis—conducted jointly with the strategic studies program—of possible NATO futures under changing economic and political conditions, an investigation of how these futures might influence U.S. commitments and forces, and a study of some Mutual Balanced Force Reduction questions as they relate to these futures. Part of our effort is directed toward developing a better understanding of total air/ground force performance in these changing environments—an effort that will require the development of some new methodology.

Logistics

In 1951 there were about 20,000 aircraft in the Air Force's operational inventory; today there are 10,000, and in the 1980s the number may decline to half of that. Even so gross a dimension as force size can have an impact on the relevance of logistics policies, particularly as they relate to the levels or echelons at which logistics decisions and activities take place. Further, the introduction of automated management and command-control and communication systems is likely to bring about significant changes in logistics policies and organizations in the decade ahead.

In addition, recent Rand work on levels of maintenance has pointed to the desirability of some reallocation of workload in aircraft maintenance between base and depot. Research on the maintenance of communications-electronics-meteorological (CEM) equipment has indicated the benefits of greater centralization of component repair for new CEM equipment. For all these reasons, Rand is reexamining the basic ways for providing logistics support in the 1980-1990 time period.

Other Rand work on new management techniques for expediting the flow of aircraft through programmed depot maintenance is now being field-tested at an Air Force Air Materiel Area. In another project, we are exploring the extent to which early involvement of logistics in the design of new weapon systems can reduce later logistics costs and problems.

R&D and Acquisition

In this program we have substantial research in progress to develop tools for contributing to decisions within the current acquisition institutions. This involves such activities as measuring technological advance for various kinds of hardware, determining when to do product-improvement R&D as opposed to starting a new development program, and exploring ways to reduce the life-cycle costs of a weapon system in the development phase. We are also examining some major changes in the basic institutional structures of conducting systems acquisition, including such topics as industry's approach to prototyping versus concurrency, R&D options through design teams, and various Air Force monitoring structures. A better understanding of these subjects should enable Rand to help the Air Force meet such challenges of the 1970s as channeling R&D toward systems desirable under a regime of volunteer forces and identifying R&D mechanisms for creating potential capabilities even under severely constrained acquisition budgets, in keeping with SALT agreements.

Manpower, Personnel, and Training

The Air Force of the seventies is faced with many changes in the way it deals with its most important resource, people. Paramount among these changes are the elimination of the draft, the reduction in defense personnel and budgets, the increasing costs of personnel and personnel-related services, and the personnel implications of an ever-increasing technological base. In addition, such things as changing racial attitudes, a declining civilian manpower pool, and new attitudes toward the military in the Congress and among the general population in the wake of the Vietnam war have created a new environment in which the Air Force has to operate. Rand's manpower program is aimed at providing the Air Force with research that is timely and useful in the analysis of the major issues of the day and in the decade to come, and that meets the Air Force's concern for the efficient use and management of its human resources.

Supporting Research

This program serves several purposes: It develops new methodology that will meet the future needs of the other programs and, in some cases, will contribute to the in-house analytic capability of the Air Force; it does the initial exploratory studies that might later become parts of the other programs; and it includes surveys and state-of-the-art assessments to keep the research staff current in technical fields. Major groups of studies include *Science and Technology* (electronics, aerodynamics, environmental studies); *Analytical Methodology* (modeling, simulation languages, mathematical and economic analyses that collectively develop new methods and approaches to Air Force problems); *Operational Concepts* (studies of Air Force operations to support other programs); and *Information Sciences* (studies related to Air Force use of existing and new computer systems, new techniques for exploiting computer power in analyses).

NATIONAL SECURITY RESEARCH: OFFICE OF THE SECRETARY OF DEFENSE

Part of Rand's national security research is conducted for the Defense Advanced Research Projects Agency (ARPA), the Director of Defense Program Analysis and Evaluation (DDPA&E), the Office of the Director of Defense Research and Engineering (DDR&E), the Defense Nuclear Agency, and the Defense Communications Agency. Other work is performed for the Department of State, the Central Intelligence Agency, and the National Security Council.

Area Studies

We are studying U.S. security interests in two broad geographical/political areas: Europe and Asia. One concern in Europe is the possible effects of Mutual Balanced Force Reduction (MBFR) on NATO conventional capabilities in the key center region. The aim is to demonstrate, through various force restructurings and other measures, how MBFR personnel cuts could be absorbed while still meeting current U.S. goals for conventional NATO defense. Other studies touch on the assumptions underlying U.S. general-purpose force planning and equipping, and on alliance commitments and peacetime force postures as the United States applies the Nixon Doctrine. We are examining European plans to use territorial defenses and how this may affect U.S. military policies.

Rand's Asian security studies include work on projections of China's military potential to the year 1980, including implications for American security policies with respect to China and other Asian countries; appropriate U.S. Asian strategies and force postures; and the effects of Chinese economic and military developments on the USSR and Japan.

Military Analysis

We are studying implications of the introduction of precision guided munitions (PGMs) for future operations, force effectiveness, and weapon systems development. We are also looking at alternative concepts of tactical nuclear warfare, attempting to identify areas where advanced technology can improve tactical nuclear capabilities. Finally, we are developing a computer simulation model that would measure the influence of weapons and tactics on fire fights involving mixed armor and infantry at the company-through-brigade levels.

Information Processing Techniques

Techniques are being developed at Rand for analyzing and upgrading the performance of complex computer networks. The aim is to improve computer efficiency and flexibility in handling the changing and time-critical command-control functions of military systems. In addition, computer support is being provided to the Worldwide Military Command and Control System.

We are conducting climate-dynamics research aimed at identifying the determinants of climate and the extent to which it might be changed by man's activities. Several computer models are being developed that describe the physical processes and their interrelationships. The models are designed for eventual solution on the ILLIAC IV, ARPA's very large, high-speed parallel processor.

Comparative Technology

We are examining the security issues likely to confront the United States when advanced technology is made more freely available to the Soviet Union and China through international trade and other transactions. We are also making comparisons of gross national product, national security expenditures, and research and development programs in the United States and the Soviet Union, emphasizing key technologies and weapon systems affecting the military balance of power between the two nations. Research on "equivalent" U.S. and Soviet military and space systems has been performed as a basis for comparative costing and evaluation.

Rand is providing ARPA with information on selected new developments in Soviet science and technology, such as the effects of nuclear explosions, heavy-current particle beams, high-power lasers, geosciences research, and superconductivity.

Advanced Technology

Our work in advanced technology covers strategic, tactical, and marine technology. In the strategic area we are studying weapon system vulnerabilities, global communications and early warning, and strategic surveillance. We are also studying the effects of nuclear-burst environments on military communication systems, helping to formulate programs on communications and propagation effects, and serving on special study committees and panel groups concerned with communications in a nuclear environment.

Our tactical studies include the preparation of a reference volume on the effects of atmospheric turbulence on laser systems operating in the lower atmosphere, and recommendations for research and development programs in millimeter-wave technology and military systems applications. We are examining guidance and navigation techniques for PGMs, and general-purpose forces weapons concepts and systems effectiveness.

In the area of marine technology, we are studying global and tactical means of communication for submarine operations, and Soviet naval mine warfare.

Concern over the possible effects of energy shortages on maintaining national security has led us to start a major study covering the following areas: DOD energy-related issues arising from an energy crisis in the United States; identification of alternative military strategies for coping with energy austerity; delineating new military missions and equipment suggested by an energy-austere environment; and identifying long-term R&D requirements for military systems and operations designed to lessen the impact of an energy crisis.

Human Resources

Our research on military training and manpower management is aimed at developing techniques for dealing with accession,

retention, retirement, and promotion problems, and with such
individual characteristics as education, job preference, length
of service, and training. We are examining the transition to an
all-volunteer force, applications of computer technologies to
training, and possible tradeoffs between equipment and
manpower.

DOMESTIC RESEARCH PROGRAMS

During 1972, the Domestic Programs Division continued to grow, with primary focus on seven major programs: Communications Policy, Education and Human Resources, Energy Policy, Health Sciences, Housing, Transportation and the Environment, and Urban Policy. Research on criminal justice, information privacy, and economic applications of game theory is also in progress, as is work in space and planetary sciences. Research and personnel of The New York City–Rand Institute also fall within the purview of this Division.

Communications Policy

The Communications Policy Program is concerned with government regulatory policy, with problems and opportunities posed by different patterns of ownership of communications media, with new and expanded uses of communications technology, and with long-term projections of technology and applications.

Recent research has been devoted to cable television. Twelve reports, published in 1972, deal with such matters as cable system franchising, educational and community uses of cable, and questions of ownership, operation, and regulation. In a joint research effort with the New York Metropolitan Regional Council, we are also evaluating uses of a two-way microwave video system to connect government agencies in 17 counties within New York, New Jersey, and Connecticut.

During 1972-1973, we will focus our research on three areas. The first, an assessment of knowledge about the effects of government interaction with the mass media, will require collection and analysis of information on the concentration of ownership and control in the mass media.

The second area concerns other federal policy problems, and will include analysis of the Fairness Doctrine in television broadcasting, of questions of broadcast-station-license renewal policies, and of the effects of the Prime Time Access Rule enforced by the Federal Communications Commission.

The third area is that of the future demand for scarce radio spectrum space by television and other electronic communication services, including the influence of new technologies, population growth and distribution, and other factors.

Education and Human Resources

In this program we are looking for ways to improve both effectiveness and efficiency in the use of resources in the educational system. During the past year, our research perspective has broadened to include issues of equal educational opportunity, educational process analysis, and research on schools as nonmarket organizations.

We approach problems of *education* by way of six research channels: evaluation of experimental or innovative programs in schools; analysis of educational effectiveness; improving resource-use effectiveness in schools; educational research and development policy; educational finance; and educational technology. Our work on *human resources* concerns the effects of vocational education and training on employability, earnings, career choice, and mobility; the theory and facts of racial discrimination; and the effect of national policy on disadvantaged workers.

The design and conduct of evaluations of experimental or innovative programs is a major area of Rand educational research. Our staff is engaged in an evaluation of its own design of a large-scale social innovation in elementary education, the OEO-sponsored Voucher Demonstration. We will describe and assess the political, social, economic, and educational outcomes of the Demonstration and the implications for education policy.

For the past three years we have conducted research under Ford Foundation sponsorship on the design and evaluation of new school financial systems, including new formulas for channeling state aid to local districts and alternative provisions for raising school revenue. Under the same sponsorship we have been working, in collaboration with the California State Department of Education, on the financial and educational implications of recent court decisions (e.g., *Serrano*

v. *Priest)*, which hold that school district spending cannot be related to the relative wealth or poverty of school districts within a state.

Under contract with the U.S. Office of Education, Rand prepared plans for the National Institute of Education, including possible objectives, program, organization, network of relationships, and initial activities of the Institute. Currently, under a grant from the Carnegie Corporation, we are developing an agenda for educational research and development. The agenda is intended to provide a conceptual framework for a national research and development strategy in education, a systematic reconciliation of the demand and supply functions for innovation in education, and guidelines for implementing the results of research and development programs.

Also under way in this program are (1) a statistical analysis to identify schools whose students consistently outperform those in other schools, adjusted for socioeconomic status, with respect to standardized test scores; (2) work on modeling the educational personnel system for use by the U.S. Office of Education in developing policies to improve the quality of educational personnel; (3) development of student choice models to assist colleges and universities in dealing with admissions and resource allocation issues; and (4) a comprehensive analysis of public and private programs for handicapped youth designed to increase the effectiveness of services and service delivery to this group.

New studies include

- ☐ An evaluation of federally funded programs aimed at bringing about innovation in the public schools.
- ☐ The design of a longitudinal study of school desegregation.
- ☐ The development of an evaluation design for Head Start programs.
- ☐ A review of the literature on mid-career education aimed toward improvement of federal policies and programs.

Energy Policy

Economic development and expansion of urban complexes imply new demands for energy. The domestic component of the Energy Policy Program is focused on the underlying cause of the conflict between energy and the environment—the rapid increase in demand for energy in all its forms—and on the implications of this conflict for governmental policymaking. Our research seeks to identify and analyze the interconnections and interactions that accompany decisions on energy source choices and growth rates in demand.

Recently completed research includes

- A series of estimates of the demand for electricity for the California State Resources Agency for a variety of alternative futures. The estimates were used as inputs to a 20-year plan for siting power plants.
- An evaluation of alternative siting options for power plants in California to define the criteria and methods that are of value to a state siting agency in the site-selection process. We also sought to identify and assess the alternatives to a power plant siting agency; the critical issues in establishing effective policy in this field; and the alternative structures, functions, and procedures for a siting agency. This work was performed under a contract with the Committee on Planning and Land Use of the California State Assembly, with support from The Rockefeller Foundation.
- Also under California Assembly sponsorship, augmented by our National Science Foundation energy studies grant, an analysis of the need for new state policies to slow the growth in demand for electricity, including estimation of the potential effectiveness of policies designed to slow the growth rate and evaluation of the potentially important side effects of a slowdown in electricity growth.

Our work on energy policy under National Science Foundation sponsorship focuses on developing improved methods for estimating future energy consumption patterns; on applying these methods to evaluate the effects of new technology, price changes, and policy actions; and on examining the benefits and costs of measures for conserving energy. Now entering the fourth year of this research, we plan to emphasize the study of energy conservation measures, policies to implement them, and the degree to which consumers would respond to energy-conserving options.

Health Sciences

The aim of this program is to improve the equity, efficiency, and effectiveness of health care delivery. We have research in progress in five broad areas, each of which is discussed briefly below.

The first of these is *health policy issues of general importance.* The work here is directed toward

- ☐ Establishing the relationships between the methods used to finance health care and the quality, quantity, and distribution of services consumed as a result.
- ☐ Estimating the nation's requirements for health manpower, and evaluating alternative methods of meeting them.
- ☐ Improving state and local government health programs.
- ☐ Determining the costs and benefits of using advanced technology in health care delivery.

The second area is the *operation of components of the health services delivery system.* Since 1970, for example, Rand has been doing research on the effects of alternative health insurance programs. This work included analysis of data accumulated by private and public insurance programs—an approach that yielded improved ways to predict the consequences of health financing programs. There are severe limitations to retrospective analysis, however, because data needed to answer many important policy questions have not been collected. To help solve this problem, Rand designed an experiment to determine the impact of different health insurance plans and coverages on the demand for health care services and to clarify the relationship between consumption of such services and individual health status. Field operations have begun in Dayton, Ohio, the first of several planned sites.

We are also examining the effects of existing and proposed federal policies on the health manpower training system. And we are reviewing the factors that lead physicians to choose between practice in rural and urban areas.

The third research area is *new methods of disease prevention, diagnosis, and treatment.* Because the nation has invested more than $20 billion in biomedical research and development since 1950, while morbidity and mortality indices have improved only slightly, we have undertaken a study of national policies and experience in medical R&D. Initially, this research is concentrating on the costs, effectiveness, and benefits of alternative advanced technology systems in the prevention, diagnosis, and treatment of major vascular diseases. We are also seeking to improve techniques for the operational delivery of health care, focusing on facilities such as coronary care units and emergency rooms.

To find an improved method for treating leukemia patients with new drugs, we have built mathematical models to simulate cellular kinetics and their response to the drugs. Closely allied with this chemotherapy research is an effort to develop a computer-based decision-aiding system to improve physician judgment, intuition, and clinical experience in research and patient management during the treatment of acute myelogenous leukemia.

Broader work on computer-assisted clinical decisionmaking seeks both to aid the practicing physician in determining the sequence of decisions he needs to make in choosing the best program for restoring a patient's health and to assist the clinical investigator by identifying and characterizing the intellectual tasks and information flows of the clinical research process.

Research in the fourth area of health services, *physiologic mechanisms of health and disease,* seeks to improve understanding of the fundamental processes of life and disease. It includes

☐ Applying analytic methods from the physical, engineering, and mathematical sciences to biochemical subsystems and the physiological mechanisms involved in clinical measurements and diagnosis.

☐ Studying the human visual system to increase the effectiveness with which information can be transmitted to man.

☐ Developing the Rand prototype closed circuit television system to aid the visually handicapped.

The fifth study area is *population behavior*. Here, we are continuing work on

☐ Building an analytical framework to assess the regional effects of income maintenance legislation.

☐ Examining welfare reform as it relates to family decisionmaking.

☐ Developing techniques for estimating labor supply functions for part-time workers.

☐ Building a model for projecting future patterns of population redistribution and for estimating the effect of alternative redistribution policies.

☐ Studying fertility and family decisionmaking in less-developed countries.

☐ Assessing the effects of alternative policies on the composition of U.S. interregional migration flows.

Housing

Most programs of housing assistance for low-income families channel public funds directly to the suppliers of housing, on condition that the housing be occupied by low-income tenants. Increasing concern over the effectiveness of this method of subsidy has led to a search for alternative means of assuring low-income families access to decent, well-maintained housing. One such means is to provide a housing allowance directly to low-income families, and so enable them to compete for housing services in the local housing market. For a number of years, Rand researchers have worked on the housing allowance concept focused initially on the housing problems of New York City.

Because there is uncertainty and even basic disagreement among housing economists and others about the effects of a national housing allowance program, the Department of Housing and Urban Development is sponsoring a series of Housing Assistance Experiments to clarify these effects. In the spring of 1972, Rand was asked to design and implement the "supply" experiment, the largest and most complex of the series. It is designed to reveal the dynamics of market response to a major increment of low-income housing demand by actually "injecting" the demand increment into entire housing markets and monitoring those markets for several years thereafter. Critical questions to be answered by the experiment include those about the effectiveness of the program as a means of inducing housing improvements and the related possibilities for inflation in housing prices; about the behavior of market intermediaries and others in an allowance-stimulated market; about residential mobility induced by the program and the consequent redistribution of local populations; and about the effects of the program on nonrecipients and their attitudes toward it.

The experimental results (to be obtained over an estimated five-year period in each of two small metropolitan areas) will be analyzed as they relate to the optimal design of a national housing allowance program and to its pros and cons relative to other forms of housing or general income subsidy for low-income households. Preliminary design of the experiment has been completed, and preparations for field operations are under way.

Transportation and the Environment

In this program we are concerned, first, with future technical options in transportation systems and their effects on the environment. One result of our work is a "system impact assessment" methodology that analyzes a broad range of effects and provides guidance for R&D decisions. We have used it to examine alternative measures to the 80-percent gas-rationing measure proposed to enable the Greater Los Angeles area to meet the clean air standards of 1977. We have also used it to analyze alternative ways to reduce air pollution to levels consistent with or better than the 1975 federal and state standards in San Diego County.

The technique, which provides estimates of economic, service, and social effects as well as of physical impacts, has also been used to provide R&D policy guidance to the U.S. Department of Transportation on short-haul transportation systems in the California corridor.

For the Transportation Systems Center of the Department of Transportation, we completed costing of three different variations of a 1972 air traffic management system. The study evaluated some of the specific benefits offered by the new system. The work should be useful in establishing R&D transportation budgets in future years.

We have also been at work on a computational model for simulating three-dimensional transient flows and water-quality parameters (including temperature) in waterways and water bodies. The model should be economically practical and applicable to a large class of problems. A forerunner model is being used to assess water policy problems in three bays with very different characteristics—Jamaica Bay, New York; Tampa Bay, Florida; and Port Royal Sound, South Carolina—as well as in estuaries of The Netherlands.

Urban Policy

Rand has undertaken a series of interrelated projects for the systematic analysis of urban policy problems. The work, sponsored by the National Science Foundation, is designed to

☐ Provide assistance to local policymakers in designing and choosing policies to meet current and future problems.

☐ Analyze common features of urban problems to assist national decisionmakers in the design of a conscious national "urban policy."

☐ Assist local governments and universities to continue analytical work after these specific projects have been completed.

Analysis is being conducted on specific problems in three urban areas: in San Jose, on the control and direction of explosive urban growth; in Seattle, on the adaptation to severe economic reversal; and in St. Louis, on the cause, effects, and control of decline of the central city.

Findings of our San Jose work indicate that inadvertent national urban policy, including such factors as mortgage insurance, tax incentives, and interstate highway construction, together with constraints and initiatives set up by state policies, create great difficulty for the local management of local policy problems. Nonetheless, growth in San Jose has become less explosive and is now relatively well controlled. What may be more troublesome in the future is the set of problems brought about by the fact that two decades of growth have failed to improve the situation of the Mexican-American minority in San Jose in relation to the Anglo majority.

In Seattle, the initial finding has been that the local economy has shown remarkable resilience in the face of massive shock from layoffs in the aerospace industry. After early anticipations of severe economic trauma, normally responsive sectors dropped less than had been feared, and the economy is now recovering without major recovery in aerospace employment. Initial findings will suggest policy options that might promote continued growth while insulating the economy as much as possible against future economic shock.

In St. Louis, three alternative futures are projected: continued decline of the central city toward bankruptcy; stabilization of the city, but as one suburb among many in the metropolitan area; or revival of a central city economic function. There seems to be little chance for any policy action to attain the last alternative, and even prevention of accelerated decline will require policy solutions that involve larger jurisdictions than that of the City of St. Louis.

Other Research

In addition to these programs, Rand's domestic research includes

- ☐ A study of the criminal justice process in Los Angeles County.
- ☐ Research on measures to ensure privacy in the computer age.
- ☐ A study of the economic applications of game theory.
- ☐ Refinement of a planet-wide geodetic control net of Mars based on Mariner 9 television pictures.
- ☐ An analysis of the feasibility of obtaining fresh water from Antarctic icebergs.

THE NEW YORK CITY–RAND INSTITUTE

The research effort at the Institute encompasses nearly all of the problems that plague urban areas today. Recently, the Institute was retained to conduct a study by the attorneys for both the plaintiffs and the defendants in a civil suit in Federal District Court. The study was a comparison of the Civil Service selection procedures for police candidates by ethnic group. It disclosed significant differences in performance by white and minority group examinees on the written test, but only slight differences in performances in other parts of the process.

In other law enforcement research, Institute staff compared the background characteristics of a large group of officers in the New York City Police Department with available measures of their performance on the job to determine the type of candidate who is likely to display specific patterns of performance.

As a result of the work done on the deployment of fire resources for the New York City Fire Department, Institute researchers developed a computer-based method for determining relocations. This method allows a great quantity of information on fires and fire-fighting equipment to be quickly examined for generation and comparison of alternative allocation plans for responding to fire emergencies.

One of the objectives of the Institute is to improve the use of data in urban policy analysis. The widespread interest in the problem of public assistance suggests that welfare information in particular be subject to scrutiny. A preliminary look at the welfare information contained in the 1970 census of population for New York City, undertaken in the course of doing research for the City's Human Resources Administration, disclosed that the 1970 census of population undercounted the number of welfare cases in New York City during 1969 by 40 percent, and underestimated the amount of welfare income received in New York City during 1969 by 40 percent.

The Institute's health-related research has focused on the factors influencing the demand for medical services. In a study sponsored jointly by the Office of Economic Opportunity and the Health Services Administration of New York City, the determinants of the demand for medical services by type of provider were examined. A major purpose of the study was to anticipate the factors that may ration demand as money prices become less significant—because of either the continued spread of health insurance or the adoption of National Health Insurance.

Other Institute research has been concerned with maintenance and operating costs of rental housing, operations of hospital emergency rooms, reform of the corrections system, local participation in governmental decisionmaking, congestion and delay in the courts, water pollution, and postgraduate education.

THE RAND GRADUATE INSTITUTE
FOR POLICY STUDIES

The Rand Graduate Institute was founded in 1970 to provide advanced graduate training leading to a doctoral degree in policy analysis—the application of scientific methods to problems of public policy, using techniques and approaches drawn from several disciplines. The Rand Corporation has become a national center of multidisciplinary policy research on the kinds of problems that public leaders face in making policy choices. Consequently, a formal effort in graduate education to impart methods and skills useful in such research was considered closely complementary to Rand's other efforts in informing and strengthening the judgments of those responsible for setting public policy. Within Rand's research environment, the Institute seeks to make a small, but distinctive, contribution to meeting the growing national need for trained policy analysts through an innovative program that combines academic rigor with relevance to issues in public policy.

Rand's Graduate Institute is an integral part of The Rand Corporation. The Institute's 3-year curriculum couples on-the-job training in a unique research environment with formal academic training in techniques and concepts drawn from different disciplines of importance in policy research. The academic year consists of three quarters of 10 weeks each. Core courses, dealing with concepts and theory and with tools and techniques useful in policy research, are offered each quarter. In addition, a series of policy analysis workshops is scheduled in which completed policy studies are reviewed in detail from a "lessons-learned" standpoint, considering data, methods, findings, client interactions, and impacts on policy.

Core courses include microeconomics, macroeconomics, statistics and data analysis, econometrics and computer applications, organizational behavior, sociological and political aspects of policy analysis, game theory, decision theory, program budgeting, and technology and public policy. Recent workshops focused on research and development, health studies, human resources, education, strategic studies, transportation and communications, and international development and foreign aid studies.

As part of the on-the-job training, graduate Fellows participate as apprentice members of research teams engaged in Rand policy studies. This training is intended, by the third year, to lead to a publishable dissertation.

The Institute's admission requirements include a Master's degree in some field of physical science, social science, or mathematics, with an adequate knowledge of all three. Of the 32 graduate Fellows now in the Institute, half were regular Rand staff members before entering the program; the remainder are from outside Rand, and their proportion has been increasing. In the fall of 1972, four new Fellows were admitted from Rand, and four from outside. Of the class admitted in the fall of 1973, over two-thirds were from outside Rand.

The faculty of the Institute is drawn from the larger Rand staff, together with outside visiting faculty. Rand researchers have strong ties with the academic world, and for many years a considerable number have continued to teach part-time in colleges and university graduate schools. In addition to interaction with Institute faculty, the students benefit from consultation with other staff members, as well as with Rand's outside consultants.

Two advisory boards have been set up to assist the Director and faculty in formulating the Institute's policies and to advise on matters relating to curriculum, faculty, admissions, qualifying examinations, and funding. The internal Rand Advisory Board meets monthly and consists of faculty members, other senior members of the Rand research staff, and students. The Academic Advisory Board meets twice a year and is headed by Harold D. Lasswell, Professor Emeritus of Law at Yale University. The Academic Advisory Board is made up of nine distinguished scholars and helps to provide a link between the academic community and the Rand Graduate Institute. Other links are provided by interaction with The Rand Corporation Board of Trustees, visiting faculty and lecturers, and outside participants on the Ph.D. qualifying examination panels and dissertation committees.

Early in 1973, the Institute was one of several universities to receive a grant from The Ford Foundation to further graduate programs in the field of policy analysis. The Ford grant of $150,000 is to be used for curriculum development, visiting lecturers and faculty, publications, and other purposes.

In June 1972, the Institute was recognized by the Accrediting Commission for Senior Colleges and Universities of the Western Association of Schools and Colleges as a candidate for accreditation.

Adminis-tration

*Board of Trustees/Former Trustees/
Administration and Research*

4

FORMER TRUSTEES

ADMINISTRATION AND RESEARCH

CORPORATE OFFICERS

Donald B. Rice, *President*

J. Richard Goldstein, *Senior Vice President*
Gustave H. Shubert, *Vice President*

George K. Tanham, *Vice President, Washington Operations*
John P. White, *Vice President*

Stephen P. Jeffries, *Secretary*

J. Scott King, Jr., *Treasurer*

RESEARCH DEPARTMENTS

Economics, Charles Wolf, Jr.
Engineering Sciences, William B. Graham
Information Sciences and Mathematics, Peter Weiner

Management Sciences, Gene H. Fisher
Physical Sciences, Victor Gilinsky
Social Science, Paul Y. Hammond

Publications, Jack Vogel
Rand Computation Center, Roderic M. Fredrickson

The Rand Graduate Institute
Charles Wolf, Jr., *Director*

RESEARCH PROGRAMS

DOMESTIC PROGRAMS DIVISION

Gustave H. Shubert, *Vice President*
L. B. Rumph, *Deputy Vice President*
Roger E. Levien, *Deputy Vice President (Washington)*
Mary E. Anderson, *Executive Assistant*

Communications Policy,
Leland L. Johnson

Education and Human Resources,
John Pincus

Energy Policy, Fred S. Hoffman

Health Sciences,
Marshall A. Rockwell, M.D.

Housing, Charles E. Nelson

Transportation and the Environment,
Howard W. McFarland

Urban Policy, Robert A. Levine

NATIONAL SECURITY/PROJECT RAND DIVISION

George K. Tanham, *Vice President*
William E. Hoehn, Jr., *Deputy Vice President*
Stephen T. Hosmer, *Deputy Vice President (Washington)*

General Purpose Forces, Philip M. Dadant,
William B. Graham, Dale M. Landi

Logistics, Murray A. Geisler

Manpower, Personnel, and Training,
Bernard D. Rostker

R&D and Acquisition, Alvin J. Harman

Strategic Forces, Victor Gilinsky,
William B. Graham, Paul Y. Hammond,
Theodore M. Parker

NATIONAL SECURITY/OSD DIVISION

John P. White, *Vice President*
Claude R. Culp, *Deputy Vice President*
Stephen T. Hosmer, *Deputy Vice President (Washington)*
Cesar Lopez, Jr., *Executive Assistant*

Atmospheric Sciences, R. Robert Rapp

Computer Sciences, Peter Weiner

Energy Policy, Fred S. Hoffman

Engineering Technology, C. C. Mow

Manpower, Personnel, and Training,
Richard V. L. Cooper

Marine Technology, Paul Tamarkin

R&D and Acquisition, Alvin J. Harman

The New York City – Rand Institute
Bernard R. Gifford, *President*

September 1973

Financing

Research Sponsors/Accountants' Report
January 1972 through June 1973

MAJOR SPONSORS OF RAND RESEARCH, 1972-1973*

United States Air Force
Defense Advanced Research Projects Agency
Office of the Assistant Secretary of Defense, International
   Security Affairs
Office of the Director of Defense Program Analysis and
   Evaluation
Office of the Director of Defense Research and Engineering
Defense Communications Agency
Defense Nuclear Agency
National Security Council
Central Intelligence Agency
Department of State
Agency for International Development
National Institutes of Health, DHEW
Office of Education, DHEW
Health Services and Mental Health Administration, DHEW
Social and Rehabilitation Service, DHEW
Office of the Secretary, DHEW
Department of Housing and Urban Development
Economic Development Administration, Department of
   Commerce
Office of Water Resources Research, Department of the
   Interior
U.S. Geological Survey, Department of the Interior
Law Enforcement Assistance Administration, Department of
   Justice
Department of Transportation
Environmental Protection Agency
National Science Foundation
Office of Economic Opportunity
Commission on Bankruptcy Laws of the United States
National Aeronautics and Space Administration
Carnegie Corporation of New York
The Ford Foundation
The John and Mary R. Markle Foundation
The Robert Wood Johnson Foundation
The Rockefeller Foundation
City of New York
State of California

San Diego County
Metropolitan Regional Council of New York
Jet Propulsion Laboratory, California Institute of Technology
The Netherlands Rijkswaterstaat

---

* Contracts and grants of more than $50,000.

ACCOUNTANTS' REPORT

Peat, Marwick, Mitchell & Co.
CERTIFIED PUBLIC ACCOUNTANTS
555 SOUTH FLOWER STREET
LOS ANGELES, CALIFORNIA 90071

The Board of Trustees
The Rand Corporation:

We have examined the statement of financial position of
The Rand Corporation (a nonprofit organization) as of June 30,
1973, and the related statements of operations and funds
retained and changes in financial position for the eighteen
months then ended. Our examination was made in accordance
with generally accepted auditing standards, and accordingly
included such tests of the accounting records and such other
auditing procedures as we considered necessary in the
circumstances.

In our opinion, the aforementioned financial statements
present fairly the financial position of The Rand Corporation
at June 30, 1973, and the results of its operations, changes in
its funds retained and financial position for the eighteen
months then ended, in conformity with generally accepted
accounting principles applied on a consistent basis.

Peat, Marwick, Mitchell & Co.

August 7, 1973

Statement of Financial Position
June 30, 1973

Current assets:	
Cash..	$1,174,365
Receivables:	
Contract operations.....................................	2,110,238
Miscellaneous..	102,770
The New York City–Rand Institute, Inc. (Note 2)..........	631,774
Total Receivables	2,844,782
Costs and accrued fees not yet billed (fees: $540,500)..........	1,572,622
Prepayments, travel advances, and deposits.................	295,182
Total Current Assets	5,886,951
Current liabilities:	
Current maturity of note payable	222,222
Accounts payable..	700,419
Employee payroll deductions.............................	312,745
Accrued expenses:	
Salaries..	460,913
Vacation pay earned.................................	1,804,086
Payroll taxes and retirement contributions	82,800
Property taxes..	38,000
Unexpended portion of research grants received.............	337,196
Total Current Liabilities	3,958,381
Net Current Assets (working capital)	1,928,570
Note receivable: The New York City–Rand Institute, Inc.	
(Note 2)...	283,708
Property, plant, and equipment, at cost (Notes 1 and 7):	
Land...	1,340,198
Buildings and improvements, less accumulated depreciation	
of $3,712,797	2,444,321
Equipment, less accumulated depreciation of $1,440,017.......	3,137,864
Leasehold improvements, less accumulated amortization	
of $28,531..	66,888
Net Property, Plant, and Equipment	6,989,271
Deferred charges (Note 3):	
Software development costs...............................	269,838
Facility rearrangement, less accumulated amortization	
of $48,248..	433,324
Other...	40,129
Total Deferred Charges	743,291

Note payable, less current maturity shown above (Note 7)	1,777,778
Long-term leases and commitments and contingent liabilities (Notes 2, 4, and 8)	—
Net Assets (funds retained)	$8,167,062

Funds retained:

Ford Foundation Grant (1952)	$1,000,000
Contributions..	22,886
Retained from operations................................	7,144,176
	$8,167,062

See accompanying notes to financial statements.

Statement of Operations and Funds Retained
Eighteen months ended June 30, 1973

Revenues:

Reimbursable costs and fees earned from contract
operations $40,075,169

Less reimbursable costs (Note 6):

Salaries	13,056,648
Employee travel costs	987,837
Consultant fees, travel, and other expenses	2,668,655
Subcontracts	1,943,164
Data processing equipment rental	1,226,039
Other direct costs	526,219
Employee fringe benefits	4,654,903
Overhead (principally salaries)	13,479,521
	38,542,986

Fees earned (principally from Federal contracts) (Note 1)	1,532,183
Interest earned	79,150
Royalties from sale of books	68,088
	1,679,421

Expenses:

Operating expenses absorbed by The Rand Corporation	527,229
Interest	13,320
Overhead costs of prior periods absorbed	66,909
Other	122,570
	730,028

Earnings before Extraordinary Item	949,393

Extraordinary item: Write-off of prior years' architect fees
related to abandoned building-expansion project 138,308

Net Earnings	811,085

Contributed funds received (unrestricted) 1,000

812,085

Expenditures for The Rand Corporation-supported projects:

Research	575,470
Publications	19,653
Fellowships	31,566
Other projects	23,816
	650,505

Amount Added to Funds Retained	161,580

Funds retained, beginning of period 8,005,482

Funds retained, end of period . . . . $ 8,167,062

See accompanying notes to financial statements.

Statement of Changes in Financial Position
Eighteen months ended June 30, 1973

Funds provided:

Earnings before extraordinary item	$ 949,393
Depreciation and amortization not requiring working capital (Notes 1 and 3)	586,180
Working Capital Derived from Operations exclusive of extraordinary item	1,535,573
Extraordinary item: Write-off of prior years' architect fees related to abandoned building-expansion project: no effect on working capital........................	—
Working Capital Derived from Operations	1,535,573
Note payable, less current maturity........................	1,777,778
Disposition of property, plant, and equipment................	16,856
Contributed funds received	1,000
Note receivable: The New York City–Rand Institute, Inc......	63,221
Decrease in working capital	759,496
	$4,153,924

Funds used:

Additions to property, plant, and equipment	$2,711,880
Expenditures for The Rand Corporation-supported projects....	650,505
Additions to deferred charges.............................	791,539
	$4,153,924

Changes in components of working capital:
Increase (decrease) in current assets:

Cash...	$1,126,956
Receivables..	(1,714,777)
Costs and accrued fees not yet billed	59,074
Prepayments, travel advances, and deposits..............	(8,330)
	(537,077)

Increase (decrease) in current liabilities:

Current maturity of note payable	222,222
Notes payable to bank	(400,000)
Accounts payable......................................	281,110
Employee payroll deductions...........................	17,945
Accrued expenses......................................	295,355
Unexpended portion of research grants received..........	(194,213)
	222,419
Decrease in working capital	$ (759,496)

See accompanying notes to financial statements.

Notes to Financial Statements
June 30, 1973

---

1. **Summary of significant accounting policies.** The Board of Trustees authorized a change from a twelve-month year ended December 31 to a fiscal year ended June 30. The change was made in order to bring fiscal year planning into a better relationship with the budgetary cycle of those agencies for which services are provided. As a result of the change, the financial statements are presented for the eighteen months ended June 30, 1973.

Fee income. Fees under cost-plus-fixed-fee contracts are recognized in even amounts over the lives of the contracts.

Depreciation and amortization of property, plant, and equipment. The Corporation has consistently provided for depreciation and amortization as follows:

Classification	Method	Term
Building #1	Straight-line	30 years
Building #2	Double-declining-balance	30 years
Furniture and fixtures	Straight-line	2-20 years
Office equipment	Straight-line	4-15 years
Computer 370/158	Sum-of-the-years-digits	8 years
Computer software	Usage	—
Automotive equipment	Sum-of-the-years-digits	4 years
Leasehold improvements	Straight-line	*

Amortized over the terms of the leases, but not in excess of the useful lives.

2. **Accounts and note receivable.** The New York City–Rand Institute, Inc., a New York membership corporation, was incorporated on July 14, 1969. The Institute was formed primarily to conduct programs of scientific research and study, provide reports and recommendations relevant to the operation, planning, or administration of the City of New York, and conduct other scientific, educational, or charitable programs. The agreements to perform work for New York City agencies are tripartite, including the Institute, The Rand Corporation, and the City of New York.

The Rand Corporation provides certain personal services relating to scientific research and study, as well as administration of the Institute, on a cost-reimbursement basis. To the extent that the Institute is unable to reimburse said costs (which are carried as accounts receivable) within thirty days, The Rand Corporation's charges to the Institute include an amount equivalent to interest on such costs at the current prime rate.

In addition, The Rand Corporation has loaned the Institute funds for the purpose of acquiring certain equipment and leasehold improvements. The loan bears no interest and is payable as soon as practicable from amortization reimbursable under the New York City contracts or from other sources available to the Institute. During the period, $62,980 was received from the Institute and applied against the loan balance.

The Rand Corporation has entered into leases on certain properties which are occupied by The New York City–Rand Institute, Inc. The leases expire during

1974. Current basic rentals for these facilities approximate $295,000 per annum.

3. Deferred charges. Deferred software development costs consist of costs incurred in the development of a management information system. Management of the Corporation estimates that total costs will approximate $400,000 and will be amortized upon completion by use of the straight-line method over a period of 5 years.

Deferred facility rearrangement costs are primarily costs incurred in connection with certain building improvements and major rearranging of personnel and equipment to provide for better efficiency. Corporation management estimates that total costs of this rearrangement will approximate $550,000. Amortization, which commenced January 1, 1973, will be over a 5-year period. Amortization as of June 30, 1973, was $48,248.

4. Long-term leases. The Corporation is liable under 30-year lease agreements effective as of November 1, 1956, and June 1, 1957, covering certain land and buildings being used by the System Development Corporation, which assumed, on July 1, 1957, the payment obligations of $356,500 annually plus property taxes and insurance. The leases may be terminated at the end of the current lease year by payment of penalties of $267,250; the penalties are reduced $80,500 annually.

The Corporation occupies other property in Washington, D.C. under a long-term lease expiring in 1979. Current basic rental for the facility approximates $247,000 per annum.

5. Employee retirement plan. The Corporation has a contributory employees' retirement plan insured with Teachers Insurance and Annuity Association of America and College Retirement Equities Fund (TIAA-CREF). All employees are eligible to participate. Participation is voluntary, but no retirement benefits are credited for periods of service during which the employee does not contribute.

The corporate contribution ranges from 4% to 17% of salaries, depending on the age of the participating employee; the employee contribution is 4% of salary regardless of age. The participant starts vesting at the beginning of the fourth year of service and is fully vested at the end of the sixth year. The Corporation has reserved the right to terminate the plan at any time, but in such an event, the benefits already purchased by the participant and contributions by the Corporation would not be adversely affected. The Corporation's contributions charged to expense for the eighteen months ended June 30, 1973, totaled $1,758,500.

6. Reimbursable costs. Prior to January 1, 1972, salaries of certain administrative personnel were accumulated as a departmental administrative pool category and were allocated to individual contracts and grants as a percentage of total direct salary charges for the department and considered direct salaries. Effective January 1, 1972, the procedure was changed so that personnel who formerly comprised the administrative pool category now charge time directly to a contract or grant while performing work relative to it. The balance of their time is considered indirect costs and charged to reimbursable costs (overhead). Although there was no effect on net earnings, the result of the change in procedure was to decrease direct salaries and increase the overhead cost.

7. Note payable. On June 28, 1973, the Corporation entered into an agreement to acquire computer equipment. On July 5, 1973, the amount of $2,000,000 was borrowed from a bank to satisfy the purchase. The note, secured by the equipment purchased, is due July 5, 1982, and bears a fluctuating interest rate at one-half of one percent above the prime rate. The note payable has been reflected in the financial statements at June 30, 1973.

8. Contingent liabilities. Contract costs billed to the United States Government are subject to adjustment by the Defense Contract Audit Agency. Such costs, billed prior to January 1, 1972, have been finalized. It is management's opinion that adequate provision has been made for adjustments pertaining to costs incurred for the eighteen months ended June 30, 1973.

Publication

Research Reports/New Rand Books/
Subscription Libraries

RESEARCH REPORTS

Rand is accountable to its sponsors both for the money it spends and the soundness of its output. But it has a larger accountability as well—to the public as a whole. For this reason we have sought the widest possible dissemination of our research results, so that the accuracy, competence, and validity of the work may be examined by critics, and so that others may have the benefit of it. Rand studies are generally available within the government and, subject to security regulations, to the public at large.

Rand publications, several hundred new titles each year, are placed in subscription libraries worldwide (see listing at the end of this section). In addition, individual titles may be obtained directly from Rand at nominal cost, and from government documentation centers as well. Rand books published by university and commercial presses are available from normal commercial outlets.

Quarterly and annual indexes, with abstracts of all publications, may be found in most public and university libraries, including all subscription libraries. Other institutions, including industrial, commercial, professional, and consumer organizations, may obtain indexes directly from Rand, without charge. This year a special, cumulative 25th-year index will be published, to commemorate our anniversary.

We maintain in addition a number of special bibliographies of selected Rand publications in various subject areas. Among them are

Aerodynamics	Delphi and Long-Range
Africa	Forecasting
Arms Control	East-West Trade
China	Education
Civil Defense	Energy
Combinatorics	Game Theory
Communication Satellites	Gaming
Communication Systems	Health
Computer Simulation	Human Resources
Computing Technology	Latin America
Decisionmaking	Linguistics

Maintenance
Mathematical Programming: Applications
Mathematical Programming: Theory
Middle East
New York City–Rand Institute Publications
Operations Research Methods
Policy Sciences
Pollution
Population
Privacy in the Computer Age
Probability
Program Budgeting
Public Safety

SIMSCRIPT and Its Applications
Southeast Asia
Space Technology and Planning
Statistics
Systems Analysis: Methods, Techniques, and Theory
Television
Transportation
Urban Problems
USSR/East Europe
Water Resources
Weapon Systems Acquisition
Weather and Meteorological Studies

These bibliographies are available from Rand free of charge.

NEW RAND BOOKS

In addition to several hundred technical reports and professional papers published under our imprint in 1972-1973, the following Rand books were published by commercial or university presses:

Bruno, James E. (ed.). *Emerging Issues in Education: Policy Implications for the Schools.* Lexington, Mass.: D. C. Heath and Company, 1972.

Canby, Steven L. *Military Manpower Procurement: A Policy Analysis.* Lexington, Mass.: D. C. Heath and Company, 1972.

Cohen, Bernard, and Jan M. Chaiken. *Police Background Characteristics and Performance.* Lexington, Mass.: D. C. Heath and Company, 1973.

Coleman, James S., and Nancy L. Karweit. *Information Systems and Performance Measures in Schools.* Englewood Cliffs, N. J.: Educational Technology Publications, Inc., 1972.

Cooper, Charles A., and Sidney S. Alexander (eds.). *Economic Development and Population Growth in the Middle East,* The Middle East: Economic and Political Problems and Prospects. New York: American Elsevier Publishing Company, Inc., 1972.

Dalkey, Norman C. *Studies in the Quality of Life: Delphi and Decision-Making.* Lexington, Mass.: D. C. Heath and Company, 1972.

DeSalvo, Joseph S. (ed.). *Perspectives on Regional Transportation Planning.* Lexington, Mass.: D. C. Heath and Company, 1973.

Goldhamer, Herbert. *The Foreign Powers in Latin America.* Princeton, N. J.: Princeton University Press, 1972.

Haggart, Sue A. (ed.). *Program Budgeting for School District Planning.* Englewood Cliffs, N. J.: Education Technology Publications, Inc., 1972.

Hammond, Paul Y., and Sidney S. Alexander (eds.). *Political Dynamics in the Middle East,* The Middle East: Economic and Political Problems and Prospects. New York: American Elsevier Publishing Company, Inc., 1972.

Levien, Roger E. *The Emerging Technology: Instructional Uses of the Computer in Higher Education.* New York: McGraw-Hill Book Company, Inc., 1972.

Newhouse, Joseph P., and Arthur J. Alexander. *An Economic Analysis of Public Library Services.* Lexington, Mass.: D. C. Heath and Company, 1972.

Novick, David (ed.). *Current Practice in Program Budgeting (PPBS): Analysis and Case Studies Covering Government and Business.* New York: Crane, Russak & Company, Inc., 1973.

Pao, Yih-Hsing, and Chao-Chow Mow. *Diffraction of Elastic Waves and Dynamic Stress Concentrations.* New York: Crane, Russak & Company, Inc., 1973.

Park, Rolla Edward (ed.). *The Role of Analysis in Regulatory Decisionmaking: The Case of Cable Television.* Lexington, Mass.: D. C. Heath and Company, 1973.

Pascal, Anthony H. (ed.). *Racial Discrimination in Economic Life.* Lexington, Mass.: D. C. Heath and Company, 1972.

Quandt, William B., Faud Jabber, and Ann Mosely Lesch (eds.). *The Politics of Palestinian Nationalism.* Berkeley and Los Angeles: University of California Press, 1973.

Zasloff, Joseph J. *The Pathet Lao: Leadership and Organization.* Lexington, Mass.: D. C. Heath and Company, 1973.

SUBSCRIPTION LIBRARIES

Over 320 libraries in the United States and 30 other countries currently maintain collections of unclassified Rand publications. These collections, listed below, are provided on an annual subscription basis. They are available to library patrons on the same basis as other holdings and are subject to the same rules and regulations. Individual publications can usually be obtained by other libraries through the Interlibrary Loan Service, and subscription libraries are authorized to reproduce materials from the Rand collection for their patrons.

The date in parentheses after each university or public library listing is the initial subscription date, to indicate the depth of the holding. Complete collections are those dating from 1953, the year in which the program was established.

Subscription Libraries in the United States

ALABAMA

Auburn 36830	Auburn University, Ralph Brown Draughon Library (1965)
Montgomery 36109	Auburn University Library (1972)
University 35486	University of Alabama Library (1971)

ALASKA

Fairbanks 99701	University of Alaska, Elmer E. Rasmuson Library (1968)

ARIZONA

Flagstaff 86001	Northern Arizona University Library (1973)
Tempe 85281	Arizona State University Library (1966)
Tucson 85721	University of Arizona, Science Division Library (1965)

ARKANSAS

Fayetteville 72701	University of Arkansas Library (1970)

CALIFORNIA

Anaheim 92803	North American Rockwell Corporation
Bakersfield 93309	California State College Library (1972)
Berkeley 94720	University of California, General Library (1953)
Burbank 91503	Lockheed California Company
Canoga Park 91303	Informatics, Inc.

Chico 95926	Chico State College Library (1963)
Davis 95616	University of California Library (1969)
Dominguez Hills 90246	California State College Library (1972)
Fullerton 92631	California State College Library (1968)
Irvine 92664	University of California Library (1965)
Long Beach 90802	Long Beach Public Library (1972)
Los Angeles 90024	University of California, Engineering and Mathematical Sciences Library (1953)
Los Angeles 90007	University of Southern California Library (1965)
Monterey 93940	Naval Postgraduate School Library (1972)
Pasadena 91109	California Institute of Technology, General Library (1953)
Pomona 91768	California State Polytechnic College Library (1968)
Riverside 92507	University of California Library (1967)
Rohnert Park 94928	California State College Library, Sonoma (1970)
Sacramento 95809	California State Library (1969)
Sacramento 95819	Sacramento State College Library (1972)
San Diego 92115	San Diego State College Library (1973)
San Jose 95113	San Jose Public Library (1972)
San Luis Obispo 93401	California State Polytechnic College, Dexter Memorial Library (1970)
Santa Barbara 93102	General Electric TEMPO Library
Santa Barbara 93106	University of California Library (1968)
Santa Clara 95053	University of Santa Clara, Orradre Library (1971)
Santa Cruz 95060	University of California Library (1969)
Stanford 94305	Stanford University Libraries (1953)
Turlock 95380	Stanislaus State College Library (1973)

COLORADO

Colorado Springs 80840	U.S. Air Force Academy, Documents Library (1968)
Denver 80203	Denver Public Library (1953)
Denver 80217	Johns-Manville Corporation
Denver 80210	University of Denver Libraries (1973)
Fort Collins 80521	Colorado State University Libraries (1973)
Greeley 80631	University of Northern Colorado Library (1973)

CONNECTICUT

Middletown 06457	Wesleyan University, Olin Library (1970)
New Haven 06520	Yale University Library (1953)
Simsbury 06070	Simsbury Public Library (1972)
Storrs 06268	University of Connecticut, Wilbur Cross Library (1963)

DELAWARE

Newark 19711	University of Delaware Library (1972)

FLORIDA

Coral Gables 33124	University of Miami, Otto G. Richter Library (1967)
Gainesville 32603	University of Florida, Engineering and Physics Library (1953)
Miami 33144	Florida International University Library (1972)
Orlando 32816	Florida Technological University Library (1970)
Tallahassee 32306	Florida State University Library (1972)
Tampa 33620	University of South Florida Library (1970)

GEORGIA

Athens 30601	University of Georgia Libraries (1967)
Atlanta 30301	Coca-Cola Company
Atlanta 30332	Georgia Institute of Technology, Price Gilbert Library (1953)
Atlanta 30303	Georgia State University Library (1972)

HAWAII

Honolulu 96822	University of Hawaii Library (1953)

IDAHO

Boise 83707	Boise State College (1971)

ILLINOIS

Cahokia 62206	Saint Louis University, Parks College of Aeronautical Technology Library (1966)
Charleston 61920	Eastern Illinois University, Booth Library (1963)
Chicago 60637	University of Chicago Library (1953)
DeKalb 60115	Northern Illinois University, Swen Franklin Parson Library (1964)
Des Plaines 60016	Universal Oil Products Company
Edwardsville 62025	Southern Illinois University, Lovejoy Library (1972)
Evanston 60201	Northwestern University, Technological Institute Library (1969)
Normal 61761	Illinois State University Library (1970)
Springfield 62706	Illinois State Library (1972)
Springfield 62703	Sangamon State University Library (1966)
Urbana 61801	University of Illinois Library (1953)

INDIANA

Bloomington 47401	Indiana University Library (1966)
Indianapolis 46202	Indiana University-Purdue University, Downtown Campus Library (1971)
Lafayette 47907	Purdue University Library (1953)
Notre Dame 46556	University of Notre Dame, Memorial Library (1970)

IOWA

Ames 50010	Iowa State University Library (1953)
Iowa City 52240	University of Iowa Libraries (1953)

KANSAS

Hays 67601	Fort Hays Kansas State College, Forsyth Library (1971)
Lawrence 66044	University of Kansas Libraries (1970)
Manhattan 66504	Kansas State University Library (1965)
Wichita 67208	Wichita State University Library (1970)

KENTUCKY

Bowling Green 42101	Western Kentucky University, Helm-Cravens Library (1973)
Highland Heights 41076	Northern Kentucky State College Library (1973)
Lexington 40506	University of Kentucky Library (1953)

LOUISIANA

Baton Rouge 70813	Southern University Library (1972)
New Orleans 70122	Louisiana State University, Earl K. Long Library (1969)
New Orleans 70118	Loyola University Library (1972)
New Orleans 70118	Tulane University, Science Library (1965)

MARYLAND

Baltimore 21218	Johns Hopkins University, Milton S. Eisenhower Library (1953)
Baltimore 21204	Towson State College, Albert S. Cook Library (1972)
College Park 20742	University of Maryland, Engineering Library (1966)
Germantown 20767	Fairchild Industries

MASSACHUSETTS

Amherst 01002	University of Massachusetts Library (1967)
Boston 02117	Boston Public Library (1963)
Cambridge 02138	Harvard University, Gordon McKay Library (1953)
Cambridge 02139	Massachusetts Institute of Technology Libraries (1953)
Chestnut Hill 02167	Boston College, Bapst Library (1965)
Lowell 01854	Lowell Technological Library (1972)

MICHIGAN

Ann Arbor 48105	Kelsey Hayes Company
Ann Arbor 48104	University of Michigan, General Library (1953)
Detroit 48202	Detroit Public Library (1966)
East Lansing 48223	Michigan State University Library (1965)
Hillsdale 49242	Hillsdale College, Mossey Learning Resources Center (1973)
Kalamazoo 49001	Western Michigan University, Dwight B. Waldo Library (1965)
Marquette 49855	Northern Michigan University Library (1969)
Warren 48090	General Motors Corporation
Ypsilanti 48197	Eastern Michigan University Library (1971)

MINNESOTA

Minneapolis 55401	Minneapolis Public Library (1971)
Minneapolis 55455	University of Minnesota Libraries (1953)

MISSISSIPPI

University 38677	University of Mississippi Library (1972)

MISSOURI

Columbia 65201	University of Missouri Library (1965)
Kansas City 64110	Linda Hall Library (1953)
Kirksville 63501	Northeast Missouri State College, Pickler Library (1970)
St. Louis 63121	University of Missouri, Thomas Jefferson Library (1964)
St. Louis 63130	Washington University Libraries (1953)
St. Louis 63105	R. S. Weinberg and Associates

MONTANA
Bozeman 59715   Montana State University Library (1966)
Missoula 59801   University of Montana Library (1973)

NEBRASKA
Lincoln 68508   University of Nebraska Libraries (1953)

NEVADA
Las Vegas 89109   University of Nevada Library (1966)
Reno 89507   University of Nevada Library (1967)

NEW HAMPSHIRE
Durham 03824   University of New Hampshire Library (1971)
Hanover 03755   Dartmouth College, Baker Library (1968)

NEW JERSEY
Newark 07101   Newark Public Library (1972)
Newark 07102   Rutgers-The State University, Dana Library
                         (1972)
Princeton 08540   Princeton University Library (1953)
Trenton 08625   Trenton State College, Roscoe L. West Library
                         (1969)
Whippany 07981   Bell Telephone Labs, Inc., Library

NEW MEXICO
Albuquerque 87106   University of New Mexico, Zimmerman Library
                         (1968)

NEW YORK
Albany 12224   New York State Library (1968)
Albany 12203   State University of New York Library (1970)
Binghamton 13901   State University of New York Library (1971)
Brooklyn 11238   Brooklyn Public Library (1970)
Buffalo 14203   Buffalo & Erie County Public Library (1963)
Buffalo 14214   State University of New York, Lockwood
                             Memorial Library (1966)
Canton 13617   St. Lawrence University Library (1969)
Ithaca 14850   Cornell University Libraries (1953)
New Rochelle 10801   Iona College, Ryan Library (1973)
New York 10027   Columbia University, Engineering Library (1953)
New York 10022   General Electric Company
New York 10021   Hunter College Library (1972)
New York 10018   New York Public Library (1953)
Niagara University 14109   Niagara University Library (1970)
Rochester 14627   University of Rochester Library (1969)
Staten Island 10301   Wagner College, Horrmann Library (1972)
Stony Brook 11790   State University of New York Library (1965)
Syracuse 13210   Syracuse University Library (1965)
Utica 13502   State University of New York, Upper Division
                             College Library (1970)

NORTH CAROLINA
Chapel Hill 27514   University of North Carolina Library (1971)
Durham 27706   Duke University Library (1953)

Greensboro 27412	University of North Carolina Library (1972)
Raleigh 27607	North Carolina State University, D. H. Hill Library (1973)
Winston-Salem 27109	Wake Forest University Library (1970)

OHIO

Akron 44304	University of Akron Library (1970)
Cincinnati 45202	Public Library of Cincinnati (1969)
Cincinnati 45221	University of Cincinnati Library (1969)
Cleveland 44106	Case Western Reserve University, Sears Library (1965)
Cleveland 44114	Cleveland Public Library (1953)
Columbus 43209	Capital University Library (1972)
Columbus 43210	Ohio State University Libraries (1953)
Columbus 43215	State Library Board (1969)
Dayton 45433	Air Force Institute of Technology Library (1967)
Kent 44240	Kent State University Library (1963)
Oxford 45056	Miami University Library (1971)
Toledo 43606	University of Toledo Library (1970)

OKLAHOMA

Norman 73069	University of Oklahoma Library (1953)
Tahlequah 74464	Northeastern State College, John Vaughan Library (1972)
Tulsa 74104	University of Tulsa, McFarlin Library (1973)

OREGON

Ashland 97520	Southern Oregon College Library (1969)
Corvallis 97331	Oregon State University Library (1953)
Portland 97207	Portland State University Library (1970)
Salem 97310	Oregon State Library (1970)

PENNSYLVANIA

Harrisburg 17126	State Library of Pennsylvania (1971)
Philadelphia 19104	Drexel University Library (1971)
Philadelphia 19122	Temple University Library (1970)
Philadelphia 19174	University of Pennsylvania Libraries (1972)
Pittsburgh 15213	Carnegie Library of Pittsburgh (1953)
Pittsburgh 15213	University of Pittsburgh Library (1968)
Slippery Rock 16057	Slippery Rock State College Library (1971)
University Park 16802	Pennsylvania State University, Pattee Library (1965)
Wilkes-Barre 18703	Wilkes College, Eugene Shedden Farley Library (1972)

RHODE ISLAND

Providence 02912	Brown University Library (1953)

SOUTH CAROLINA

Clemson 29631	Clemson University Library (1973)
Columbia 29208	University of South Carolina, McKissick Memorial Library (1969)

TENNESSEE

Cookeville 38501	Tennessee Technological University Library (1972)

Knoxville 37916	University of Tennessee Library (1972)
Memphis 38111	Memphis State University, John Brister Library (1964)
Nashville 37203	Joint University Libraries (1953)

TEXAS

Austin 78712	University of Texas Library (1953)
Canyon 79015	West Texas State University Library (1970)
College Station 77843	Texas A&M University Library (1965)
Dallas 75222	Southern Methodist University, Fondren Library (1969)
Dallas 75222	Texas Instruments, Inc.
Houston 77001	Rice University Library (1958)
Houston 77004	University of Houston Libraries (1969)
Lubbock 79409	Texas Tech University Library (1969)

UTAH

Provo 84601	Brigham Young University Library (1965)
Salt Lake City 84112	University of Utah Libraries (1953-71, 1973)

VIRGINIA

Blacksburg 24061	Virginia Polytechnic Institute and State University Library (1965)
Charlottesville 22903	University of Virginia, Alderman Library (1953)
Lexington 24450	Virginia Military Institute, Preston Library (1963)
McLean 22101	The Mitre Corporation

WASHINGTON

Bellingham 98225	Western Washington State College, Wilson Library (1971)
Cheney 99004	Eastern Washington State College, John F. Kennedy Memorial Library (1972)
Olympia 98501	Washington State Library (1970)
Pullman 99163	Washington State University Library (1967)
Seattle 98124	The Boeing Company
Seattle 98105	University of Washington Library (1953)

WEST VIRGINIA

Charleston 25304	West Virginia Library Commission, Technical Services (1973)
Glenville 26351	Glenville State College, Robert F. Kidd Library (1971)
Institute 25112	West Virginia College of Graduate Studies (1972)

WISCONSIN

Green Bay 54305	University of Wisconsin Library (1967)
Madison 53706	University of Wisconsin, General Library (1953)
Menomonie 54751	University of Wisconsin-Stout, Pierce Library (1970)
Milwaukee 53233	Marquette University, Memorial Library (1972)
Milwaukee 53233	Milwaukee Public Library (1971)
Milwaukee 53202	Northwestern Mutual Life Insurance Company
Milwaukee 53201	University of Wisconsin-Milwaukee, Library (1972)

WYOMING
Laramie 82071   University of Wyoming Library (1971)

*   *   *

DISTRICT OF COLUMBIA
Washington 20310   Army Library, Department of the Army (1970)
Washington 20006   George Washington University Library (1970)
Washington 20540   Library of Congress (1953)

*   *   *

PUERTO RICO
Rio Piedras 00931   Universidad de Puerto Rico, Biblioteca General
                           (1966)

Subscription Libraries in Other Countries

AUSTRALIA
Adelaide, S.A.   State Library of South Australia (1971)
Armidale, N.S.W.   University of New England Library (1971)
Brisbane, Queensland   State Library of Queensland (1973)
Bundoora, Victoria   La Trobe University Library (1971)
Canberra, A.C.T.   Australian National University, Institute of
                           Advanced Studies Library (1968)
Canberra, A.C.T.   Defence Group Library (1969)
Canberra, A.C.T.   National Library of Australia (1969)
Clayton, Victoria   Monash University Library (1972)
Duntroon, A.C.T.   Royal Military College, Bridges Library (1968)
North Ryde, N.S.W.   Macquarie University Library (1966)
Sydney, N.S.W.   University of Sydney, Fisher Library (1958)

BAHAMAS
Nassau   Nassau Bank and Trust Company Ltd. (Library)
                           (1972)

BELGIUM
Namur   Facultes Universitaires N.D. de la Paix, Service
                           des Bibliotheques (1973)

BRAZIL
Brasilia   Camara dos Deputados (1971)
Sao Jose dos Campos   INPE Library (1972)

CANADA
Burnaby, B.C.   Simon Fraser University Library (1970)
Calgary, Alberta   University of Calgary Library (1973)
Downsview, Ontario   York University Libraries (1973)

Fredericton, N.B.	University of New Brunswick, Harriet Irving Library (1969)
Guelph, Ontario	University of Guelph Library (1968)
Halifax, N.S.	Dalhousie University Library (1968)
Hamilton, Ontario	McMaster University, Mills Memorial Library (1968)
London, Ontario	University of Western Ontario Library (1972)
Montreal, Quebec	McGill University Library (1968)
Montreal, Quebec	Sir George Williams University Library (1969)
Ottawa, Ontario	Carleton University Library (1968)
Ottawa, Ontario	Defence Research Board (1965)
Ottawa, Ontario	Department of Regional Economic Expansion Library (1973)
Ottawa, Ontario	National Research Council Library (1958)
Toronto, Ontario	University of Toronto Library (1968)
Vancouver, B.C.	University of British Columbia Library (1970)
Waterloo, Ontario	University of Waterloo Computer Library (1970)
Waterloo, Ontario	Waterloo Lutheran University Library (1972)
Windsor, Ontario	University of Windsor Library (1970)
Winnipeg, Manitoba	University of Manitoba, Elizabeth Dafoe Library (1973)

CANAL ZONE
Balboa	Canal Zone College Library (1971)

DENMARK
Aarhus C	Statsbiblioteket, Universitetsparken (1972)
Fjerritslev	Per Gundersen's Hus, Library (1972)

ENGLAND
Bailrigg, Lancaster	University of Lancaster Library (1967)
Boston Spa, Yorkshire	National Lending Library for Science and Technology (1958)
Chesham, Bucks.	National Defence College Library (1968)
London, WC2	British Library of Political and Economic Science (1971)
London, SW1A 2EU	Ministry of Defence Library (C&A) (1967)
Oxford	Institute of Economics and Statistics (1971)

FRANCE
Paris 16	Association Francaise pour la Cybernetique Economique et Technique, Library (1958)
Paris 16	Organisation for Economic Co-operation and Development, Library (1968)

GERMANY
Berlin-Charlottenburg	Universitatsbibliothek der Technischen Universitat Berlin (1969)
Bochum-Querenburg	Universitatsbibliothek der Ruhruniversitat (1967)
Bonn	Deutscher Bundestag Bibliothek (1973)
Ebenhausen-Isartel	Stiftung Wissenschaft und Politik, Library (1966)
Frankfurt a.M.	Stadt- und Universitats Bibliothek (1958)
Gottingen	Niedersachsische Staats- und Universitatsbibliothek Gottingen (1970)
Hamburg	Staats- und Universitatsbibliothek (1971)
Hannover, Welfengarten	Bibliothek der Technischen Hoschschule und Technische Informationsbibliothek (1968)

Kiel	Bibliothek des Instituts fur Weltwirtschaft and der Universitat Kiel (1973)
Koln	Universitats- und Stadtbibliothek Koln (1970)
Konstanz	Universitat Konstanz Bibliothek (1971)
Munich	Industrieanlagen-Betriebsgesellschaft (1966)
Saarbrucken	Universitatsbibliothek der Universitat des Saarlands (1969)

INDIA

Ahmedabad-15	Indian Institute of Management Library (1969)
Delhi-6	Ministry of Defence, Defence Scientific Laboratory (1967)
New Delhi-1	Indian Council of World Affairs Library (1966)
New Delhi-1	Indian Institute of Public Administration Library (1965)
New Delhi-1	Institute for Defence Studies and Analyses Library (1971)

INDONESIA

Djakarta	Centre for Strategic and International Studies (1972)

ISRAEL

Haifa	Israel Institute of Technology, Department of Industrial and Management Engineering (1965)
Tel-Aviv (Hakyria)	Defence Ministry Mamram Computer Unit Library (1966)
Tel-Aviv	Ministry of Defence (1971)
Tel-Aviv	Tel-Aviv University, Graduate School of Business and Administration Library (1965)

ITALY

Padova	Biblioteca Universitaria (1968)

JAPAN

Kamakura, Kanagawa	Nomura Research Institute (1967)
Nihonbashi Chuo-ku	Nissho Iwai Co.
Tokyo	Boei Kenshusho
Tokyo	Fujitsu KK
Tokyo	Kikai Shinko Kyokai
Tokyo	Kinokuniya/Dentsuken Library
Tokyo	Naigai Trading Co. Ltd.
Tokyo	National Diet Library (1958)
Tokyo	Nippon Suido Consultant
Tokyo	Nissho Iwai Co.
Tokyo	Seisaku Kagaku Kenkyusho
Tokyo	University of Toyko, Department of Nuclear Engineering (1972)
Toyota-shi Aichi-ken	Gijutsu Shiryo Shitsu

JORDAN

Amman	Royal Society for Scientific Research (1966)

KOREA

Seoul	Kumi Trading Co., Ltd.

LEBANON
Beirut   Institute for Palestine Studies (1972)

MEXICO
Puebla, Puebla   Universidad de las Americas, Learning Resources
                                Center Library (1972)

THE NETHERLANDS
Delft   Technological University Library (1972)

NORWAY
Trondheim   University of Trondheim, Norwegian Institute of
                                Technology (1971)

NEW ZEALAND
Wellington   General Assembly Library (1971)

PAKISTAN
Rawalpindi   Defence Science Organization, Documentation
                                Centre (1970)
Rawalpindi Cantt   National Defence College Library (1969)

SCOTLAND
Aberdeen   Aberdeen University Library (1973)

SINGAPORE
Singapore 10   Ministry of Defence (1971)

SOUTH AFRICA
Pretoria, Transvaal   Universiteit van Pretoria, Merensky-Biblioteek
                                (1971)

SPAIN
Madrid-34   Universidad Autonoma, Catedra Teoria
                                Economica (1970)

SWEDEN
Bromma 20   Systecon AB
Nykoping 1   Aktiebolaget Atomenergi Library (1958)
Stockholm 80   Defence Materiel Administration, Documentation
                                Centre and Reference Library (1968)

SWITZERLAND
St. Gallen   University St. Gallen, Institute of Business
                                Administration (1972)
Zurich   Ecole Polytechnique Federale Zurich, Library
                                (1969)

THAILAND
Bangkok   Asian Institute of Technology Library (1970)